VOCABULARY
for Achievement

Grade 4

Margaret Ann Richek

GREAT SOURCE
WILMINGTON, MA

Margaret Ann Richek

Professor, College of Education, Northeastern Illinois University; consultant in reading and vocabulary study; author of *The World of Words* (Houghton Mifflin)

Writing and Editing: Maryann Langen, Sue Paro

Text Design and Production: Publicom, Inc.

Illustrations: Rita Lascaro and Carol Maglitta

Cover Design: Publicom, Inc.

Cover Photo: John Giustina/FPG

Acknowledgments

The pronunciation key and the dictionary entries on pages 22–24 and 58: Copyright © 1998 by Houghton Mifflin Company. Reproduced by permission from The American Heritage Children's Dictionary. The Thesaurus entries on pages 81 and 84: Copyright © 1997 by Paul Hellweg. Reproduced by permission from The American Heritage Children's Thesaurus.

Printed in the United States of America

International Standard Book Number: 0-669-47127-5

1 2 3 4 5 6 7 8 9 10 - POO - 06 05 04 03 02 01

Contents

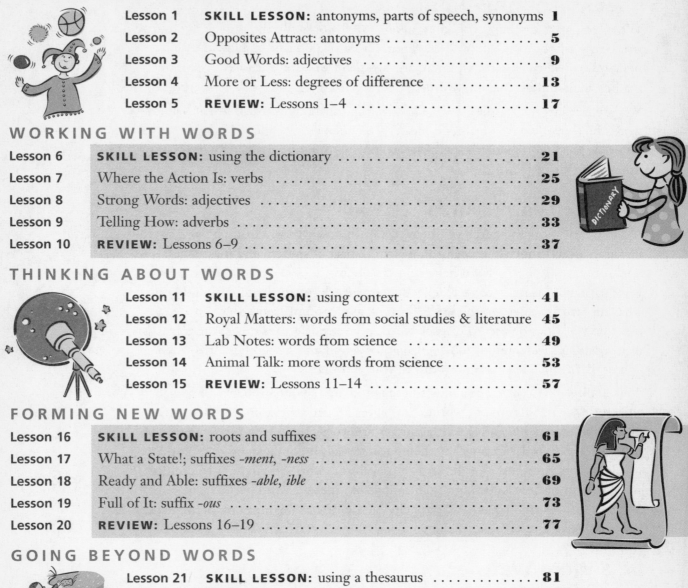

About This Book

That's a Lot of Words!

When you started school, you knew about 5,000 words. By the time you graduate from high school, you will probably know about 60,000 words! How does a person learn all those words? There are two main ways to learn new words: by reading a lot and by studying words.

You are in charge of reading a lot! However, in this book you will learn to study words by learning new words and meanings, understanding that words have different jobs to do (parts of speech), recognizing different forms of words, and using word parts.

Ways to Learn Words

A dictionary and a thesaurus will help you learn new words. For each word listed inside it, a **dictionary** tells the pronunciation, part of speech, and meaning(s). The pronunciation of a word helps you say the word. The part of speech tells whether a word is a noun, verb, adjective, or adverb. A word's definition describes what the word means and the ways it can be used. Sample sentences show you how the word can be used. For each word listed inside a **thesaurus,** there is a list of words that mean about the same thing, or synonyms. Use a thesaurus when you need a really clear, specific word in your writing.

This book will also teach you how to use antonyms, synonyms, parts of speech and word parts to figure out words. Antonyms are words that mean the opposite of each other, like *tall* and *short.* Synonyms are words that mean the same thing, like *small* and *tiny.* Learning them helps you to use and understand different words. If you can figure out the part of speech of a word, it will help you understand what it means. Knowing the meanings of different word parts, such as prefixes, suffixes, and roots, can also help you figure out the meaning of unfamiliar words.

Be a Word Watcher

As you learn new words *in* this book, look for them *outside* the book. See if you can find the words in other books, newspapers, magazines, on TV, or even on the back of a cereal box. When you find a new word, share it with your class. Maybe you'll be the one to find the most new words this year. Good luck!

Skill Lesson
antonyms, parts of speech, synonyms

Bertha Sanchez
2/9/06

Using different words can make your reading and writing more interesting. When you revise your writing, you can play around with the words you choose so that you pick the very best ones. To do this, it helps to know a lot of words. It also helps to know different kinds of words. In the next three lessons, you will learn about words that are opposites, words that describe good things, and words that mean more or less of the same thing.

 ANTONYMS Some words are opposites of each other. Have you ever been *hot* when someone else was *cold?* Did you ever feel *good*, but then felt *bad?* These words are opposites. We call opposites **antonyms.**

Below are some sentences. Look at the boldfaced word, the word in dark type, and fill in the **antonym.** The first one has been done for you.

1. **Beautiful** is the antonym of _____ugly_____ . (*ugly/rainy*)
2. **Up** is the antonym of ____**down**____ . (*warm/down*)
3. **Top** is the antonym of ____**bottom**____ . (*middle/bottom*)

To show how one thing is different from another, people use **antonyms.** An antonym can mean "not." For example, *hot* means "not cold." Sometimes, you will see the word *but* between two antonyms. Write the word that can replace the underlined words in each sentence.

4. I wanted my baby brother to be happy, but instead he was <u>not happy</u>.
____**Sad**____ (*sad/sick*)
5. The chair is hard, but the pillow is <u>not hard</u>. **Soft**
(*brown/soft*)
6. This piece of candy is big, but this one is <u>not big</u>. **little**
(*good/little*)

B POSITIVE WORDS AND NEGATIVE WORDS

Some things in our lives are good, and other things are bad. We use different words to describe good things and bad things. In the sentence below, *good* is a **positive word.** *Bad* is a **negative word.** *Good* and *bad* are antonyms.

David thought the movie was **good,** but I thought it was **bad.**

When you write or talk about something good, or positive, use words that bring good thoughts to mind. When you write or talk about something bad, use negative words.

Below are some pairs of antonyms. One word in each pair is a positive word. The other is a negative word. Write each word in the column in which it fits the best. Then add a pair of your own antonyms.

sad – happy   sick – healthy

handsome – ugly   excellent – terrible

dirty – clean   mean – kind

Positive Words	Negative Words
happy	sad
handsome	ugly
clean	dirty
healthy	sick
excellent	terrible
kind	mean

PARTS OF SPEECH The part of speech tells how a word works in a sentence. Each word in this book is listed with its part of speech. Four very important ones are **noun, verb, adjective,** and **adverb.** Each one has a different job to do. Knowing the part of speech of a word will help you understand the word and use it correctly in your writing.

A **noun** is a person, animal, place, thing, or idea.
Person: <u>Kristi</u> helps me.
Animal: Our <u>dog</u> is brown.
Place: We play in the <u>yard</u>.
Thing: The <u>ball</u> bounced.
Idea: <u>Freedom</u> is important.

An **adjective** describes a noun. It may come before or after a noun.
Before: <u>Kind</u> Kristi helps me.
After: Kristi is <u>kind</u>.

A **verb** is a word for an action or way of being.
Action verb: My father <u>drove</u> us to the mall last night.
Way of being: Mike <u>is</u> tall and thin.

An **adverb** describes a verb. It may come before or after a verb.
Before: I <u>hardly</u> noticed the rain.
After: The train stopped <u>suddenly</u>.

Try these examples. Circle the part of speech of the boldfaced word.

1. Darren **runs** a mile every day. *noun* / *verb*

2. Lisa **slowly** opened the door. *verb* / *adverb*

3. The **mail** arrived early. *verb* / *noun*

4. José is wearing a **red** sweater. *adverb* / *adjective*

5. Who **left** the ice cream on the table? *verb* / *adverb*

6. The soccer ball rolled **easily** into the net. *adjective* / *adverb*

D **ADJECTIVES** The positive and negative words in exercise B
are words that describe something. Now you know they are called
adjectives. Write the adjective that best describes the underlined
noun in each sentence.

1. I am amazed at how flamingos can stand on their long,
   skinny legs. (*skinny/hungry*)

2. Amy put a _slimy_ frog in her brother's hand. (*short/slimy*)

3. The puppy put its _wet_ nose against my leg. (*furry/wet*)

4. A porcupine's quills are _cold_ . (*sharp/cold*)

5. The skin of an elephant is all _wrinkled_ . (*red/wrinkled*)

E **SYNONYMS** Some words have the same or almost the
same meaning. They are called **synonyms.** *Cold* and *freezing* are
synonyms. Both mean a low temperature. But you would probably
rather be outside in *cold* weather than in *freezing* weather. Cold
weather is cold, but freezing weather is *really* cold! One is *more*,
and one is a bit *less*.

Words of *more* and *less* show how strongly we feel about something. Write the adjective that can replace the underlined words
in each sentence.

1. I felt **full** after the main course, but after I ate dessert, I really felt even
   more full. _Stuffed_ (*empty/stuffed*)

2. I was **happy** to get a present, but when I got two more, I was even
   more happy. _de_ (*delighted/silly*)

3. This bug is **small,** but the one we found the other day was really even
   more small. _____ (*tiny/dangerous*)

4. My ice-cream sundae was **big,** but the belly-buster sundae was even
   more big! _____ (*sweet/huge*)

Opposites Attract
antonyms

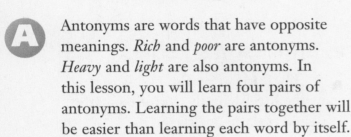

light
heavy

A Antonyms are words that have opposite meanings. *Rich* and *poor* are antonyms. *Heavy* and *light* are also antonyms. In this lesson, you will learn four pairs of antonyms. Learning the pairs together will be easier than learning each word by itself.

1. **courteous** (kûr' tē əs) *A* **courteous** *person is polite and considerate of others.* (adjective)
My **courteous** cousin always remembers to say "please" and "thank you."

2. **rude** (ro͞od) *A* **rude** *person is not polite and does not think of others.* (adjective)
The **rude** man pushed his way to the front of the ticket line.

3. **partner** (pärt' nər) *A* **partner** *is someone who works with another person in an equal way; an ally.* (noun)
My debate **partner** and I are planning our next speech.

4. **opponent** (ə pō' nənt) *An* **opponent** *is someone who competes, fights, or takes an opposite position.* (noun)
Leah defeated her **opponent** to win the race.

5. **plentiful** (plĕn' tĭ fəl) *If something is* **plentiful,** *there is more than enough of it.* (adjective)
There was a **plentiful** supply of food at the party.

6. **scarce** (skârs) *If something is* **scarce,** *there is not enough of it; it is rare.* (adjective)
School supplies are often **scarce** in poor countries.

7. **sensible** (sĕn' sə bəl) *To be* **sensible** *is to show good judgment or to make sense.* (adjective)
It is **sensible** to take an umbrella with you if it is raining.

8. **ridiculous** (rĭ dĭk' yə ləs) *Something* **ridiculous** *is silly or makes no sense.* (adjective)
It is **ridiculous** to wear a bathing suit in the snow.

Draw a line between each word and its definition.

1. rude — large supply
2. ridiculous — not polite
3. partner — silly
4. plentiful — ally
5. opponent — showing good judgment
6. sensible — polite
7. scarce — not enough
8. courteous — someone who competes

Each boldfaced word in the passage below has an antonym that is also in the passage. Read the passage. Then answer the questions that follow.

The Tortoise and the Hare, an Aesop's Fable

Long ago, there lived a hare who made fun of a tortoise because he was so slow. One day, the tortoise became tired of the hare's **rude** treatment. So the tortoise said, "My legs may be short, but I can beat you in a race." The hare laughed, "What a **ridiculous** thing to say. No **sensible** animal would think you could win over me. Let's race, and I'll leave you in the dust!"

On the day of the race, the animals came to watch the tortoise and his **opponent,** the hare. The race started, and the hare ran down the road, while the tortoise crawled along with slow, steady steps. After a while, the hare could see that he was far ahead. He said to himself, "That tortoise is miles behind me. There is a **plentiful** supply of food in that field, and I am tired from running so fast. I think I'll have a snack and then lie down in the grass."

The hare ate and soon fell asleep. As the hare slept, the tortoise quietly passed by him.

The tortoise kept walking and walking. When he was near the finish line, a friend of the hare shouted at him to wake up. As the hare ran toward the finish line, the tortoise won the race.

After the race, the hare treated the tortoise in a more **courteous** way. In fact, they became **partners** in the forest. Whenever food was **scarce,** they would share it. And they always showed respect for each other.

The moral is: Slow and steady wins the race.

WORD LIST

courteous

opponent

partner

plentiful

ridiculous

rude

scarce

sensible

1. What was the hare's biggest mistake?

_____

2. Which of these words best describes the hare: *sensible*, *rude*, *opponent*, or *partner?* Why do you think so?

_____

C For each sentence, choose the word that makes sense. Write it on the line. You will have to capitalize one word.

ridiculous, sensible

1. It's _____ to have a fire drill at the beach.

2. It's _____ to have a fire drill at school.

courteous, rude

3. If you are _____ , people are usually nice to you.

4. _____ behavior often makes people angry.

opponent, partner

5. Tanya's dance _____ stepped on her toe by mistake.

6. Connor's fast running on the soccer field helped him beat the

_____ .

D Some of the words in the word list have positive, or good, meanings. Some of them have negative, or bad, meanings. Write the words with good meanings on the "Good" side of the chart. Then, for each positive word, write its antonym on the "Bad" side of the chart.

Good	Bad
_____	_____
_____	_____
_____	_____
_____	_____

OTHER FORMS

courteously

partnership

plenty

ridiculously

rudely

rudeness

scarcely

sensibly

E Complete each sentence with a phrase that makes sense. Note that some other forms of the vocabulary words have been used.

1. It's natural to hope that your **opponent** _____

_____ .

2. I can **scarcely** believe that _____

_____ .

3. An example of something that looks **ridiculous** is _____

_____ .

4. If you have **plenty** of something, _____

_____ .

5. A person who acts **sensibly** _____

_____ .

ENRICHMENT WORDS

Here are two more words that are antonyms. Have you seen these words before?

1. **initiate** (ĭ **nĭsh'** ē āt') *To* **initiate** *is to begin.* (verb)

We often **initiate** a phone call by saying, "Hello."

2. **terminate** (tûr' mə nāt') *To* **terminate** *is to end.*

I **terminate** my phone calls by saying, "Goodbye." (verb)

OFF THE PAGE

Describe a character who is either **ridiculous** or **sensible**. Think about what your character would wear, look like, and do. Write several sentences about your character. Draw a picture of your character, too.

Good Words
adjectives

enthusiastic

 Have you ever noticed that some words can make you think of pleasant, positive things? The words below all describe things that are good, or positive.

1. **amusing** (ə myōo' zĭng) *Something that is amusing is funny in a pleasant way.* (adjective)
It's **amusing** to watch puppies play together.

2. **competent** (kŏm' pĭ tənt) *A competent person is able to do a task well.* (adjective)
The **competent** swimmer swam out to the raft easily.

3. **delectable** (dĭ lĕk' tə bəl) *Something that is delectable is very delicious.* (adjective)
My mother is making a **delectable** cake for my birthday party.

4. **elated** (ĭ lāt' əd) *When we are elated, we are very happy.* (adjective)
Josh was **elated** when he won the national writing contest.

5. **enthusiastic** (ĕn thōoz' zē ăs' tĭk) *When we are enthusiastic, we have great interest or excitement.* (adjective)
The **enthusiastic** crowd clapped and cheered for the team.

6. **fabulous** (făb' yə ləs) *Something that is fabulous is wonderful and almost seems too good to be true.* (adjective)
Topkapi Palace in Turkey has a **fabulous** collection of jewels.

7. **fortunate** (fôr' chə nĭt) *To be fortunate is to be lucky.* (adjective)
Ryan was **fortunate** that he wasn't hurt when he fell off his bike.

8. **trustworthy** (trust' wûr' thē) *A trustworthy person can be depended on.* (adjective)
My **trustworthy** friend would never repeat the secret I told him.

Draw a line between each vocabulary word and its synonym.

1. fortunate   funny
2. elated   very happy
3. fabulous   wonderful
4. amusing   lucky
5. trustworthy   excited
6. competent   able
7. enthusiastic   delicious
8. delectable   dependable

All the boldfaced words in the passage below are positive words. Read the passage. Then answer the questions that follow.

Chocolate: A Mysterious Taste

In 1519, when Spanish explorer Hernán Cortez came to Mexico, he found that the Aztecs were fond of a drink made from the cocoa bean. The cocoa beans were so valuable to the Aztecs that they even used them as money!

Cortez was **elated** about the beans, for he thought he could become rich from selling them in Spain. He filled his ships with cocoa beans and took them back home. There, people started to mix the chocolate drink with sugar. The king did not want people outside of Spain to make this drink. So, the **trustworthy** Spanish people kept the recipe a secret for many years. But after a while, people from other countries finally learned the secret of making the sweet chocolate drink. Slowly, chocolate spread to France, England, and throughout Europe. Some people even used cocoa beans to flavor candy.

People had different thoughts about chocolate. It may seem **amusing** to us today, but some people feared that chocolate was dangerous to eat and drink! Others were so **enthusiastic** about its taste that they used it as medicine.

cocoa beans

What makes the taste of chocolate so **fabulous?** It melts at the temperature of our bodies, which means that it melts in our mouths, a very pleasant feeling. Chocolate also has an appealing smell. Some shop owners have actually tried to use the smell of chocolate to bring customers inside.

It takes many steps to make chocolate from cocoa beans, so chocolate makers must be very **competent** at what they do. The cocoa beans must be dried, cleaned, roasted, crushed, and ground. But the final result is **delectable!** We are very **fortunate** that, over 400 years ago, the Aztecs introduced this food to the world.

WORD LIST

amusing
competent
delectable
elated
enthusiastic
fabulous
fortunate
trustworthy

1. How did chocolate become a popular treat in Spain?

_____

_____

2. Tell how chocolate is delectable and fabulous. Write one sentence for each word.

_____

_____

 Choose the word that best fits in each sentence. Write the word on the line.

1. When you give a speech, it's often a good idea to include an _____ story so people will laugh. (*elated*/*amusing*)

2. Matt is a _____ pitcher, but not a great pitcher. (*competent*/*amusing*)

3. The _____ , brightly colored bird spread its huge wings and flew away. (*trustworthy*/*fabulous*)

4. Ana felt _____ to have escaped from the burning building. (*delectable*/*fortunate*)

5. My teammate's mom is _____ and always remembers to pick me up and take me to practice. (*trustworthy*/*elated*)

D Adding *-ly* to a word makes it an adverb. An adverb describes an adjective, a noun, or another adverb. *Amusing*, an adjective, can become *amusingly*. *Amusingly* is an adverb that means "in an amusing way." Sometimes the final *e* is dropped when *-ly* is added. Use the model to fill in the blanks below.

Example: slowly = slow + ly

1. competently = competent + ly

2. fortunately = fortunate + ly

3. triumphantly = triumphan + ly

4. delectably = delectab + ly

Name

Date

OTHER FORMS
amuse
competently
competence
elatedly
enthusiasm
fabulously
fortunately
fortune

E Complete each sentence with a phrase that makes sense. Note that some other forms of the vocabulary words have been used.

1. If I were **fabulously** rich, I _____ .

2. It's common to show **enthusiasm** by _____ .

3. Something that I find **amusing** is, _____ .

4. **Fortunately,** Rico remembered to bring _____

_____ .

5. "Oh, wow!" said Chris **elatedly**, "I _____

_____ .

ENRICHMENT WORDS

Here are two more words that have positive meanings.

1. admire (ăd mīr') *When we* **admire** *someone or something, we respect it and think it is very good.* (verb)

   I **admire** the artist's ability to create beautiful paintings.

2. triumph (trī' əmf) *A* **triumph** *is a win or a victory.* (noun)

   After their **triumph** in the World Series, the baseball team celebrated.

OFF THE PAGE

Make a web like the one shown here to explore a word in this lesson. Think of three categories to include for your web. They can be the same as the ones shown below or different.

Other Words for Elated
happy
delighted

Antonyms for Elated
sad
disappointed

Elated

Times That I Was Elated
when I got my puppy
when I scored a goal in soccer

12 Playing with Words

© Great Source DO NOT COPY

More or Less
degrees of difference

A When you eat, do you take small bites or do you try to eat lots all at once? In other words, do you gobble or nibble? Some words have the same basic meaning. But one means *more* and one means *less*. Although *nibble* and *gobble* both mean "to eat," *nibble* is to "take small bites," and *gobble* is "to eat quickly and greedily."

1. **nibble** (nĭb' əl) *To **nibble** is to take small, quick bites from something.* (verb)
"I'm not very hungry," said Kara. "I'll just **nibble** some pretzels."

2. **gobble** (gob' əl) *To **gobble** is to eat up quickly and greedily.* (verb)
Keith was so hungry that he **gobbled** his lunch down in five minutes.

3. **annoyance** (ə noi' əns) *An **annoyance** is something that bothers you and makes you a little angry.* (noun)
The fly buzzing around my head was an **annoyance**.

4. **rage** (rāj) **Rage** *is violent or extreme anger.* (noun)
Seeing the bully pick on the small child filled Charlie with **rage**.

5. **nap** (năp) *To **nap** is to sleep lightly for a short while.* (verb)
A ten-minute **nap** will often help you stay up late.

6. **slumber** (slŭm' bər) *To **slumber** is to sleep soundly.* (verb)
I couldn't believe that my cat was able to **slumber** through the noisy party.

7. **glance** (glăns) *To **glance** is to look quickly.* (verb)
During a test I often **glance** at the clock to check the time.

8. **stare** (stâr) *When we **stare** at something we look at it long and hard.* (verb)
My grandmother told me it's not polite to **stare** at people.

Draw a line between each vocabulary word and its definition.
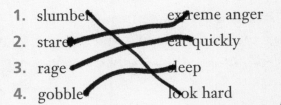
1. slumber   extreme anger
2. stare   eat quickly
3. rage   sleep
4. gobble   look hard

The Aesop's fable uses the four pairs of words you have learned that mean more or less of the same thing. Read the passage. Then answer the questions that follow.

The Country Mouse and the City Mouse

The city mouse went to visit his cousin in the country. The country mouse prepared a nice meal of bread crusts, but the city mouse only **nibbled** at it. The country mouse gave his cousin a straw bed to sleep on. But in the morning the city mouse said, "I could only **nap** for a few minutes, because that bed was so hard."

The country mouse had trouble hiding his **annoyance.** "I try to be nice to you, but you are never satisfied."

"I'm sorry," said the city mouse, "but this place is not very comfortable. Come to the city, and you will see how to eat and sleep."

So the two mice went to the city. First, they **gobbled** up the leftovers of a huge meal. There were six types of cheese, rolls, bread sticks, and even pretzels.

"This is wonderful," said the country mouse.

The country mouse then lay down on a bed of feathers and silk. He **slumbered** comfortably through the night.

The next morning the country mouse was thanking his city cousin when he happened to **glance** over his shoulder. There was a huge cat! It **stared** right at him, ready to jump.

"Let's get out of here," he cried, and both mice raced toward the safety of a hole. They made it through just as the cat's paw reached for them.

With **rage** in his voice, the country mouse said, "How dare you bring me to a place like this?" The moral is: Better a simple meal and a hard bed in safety, than a wonderful meal and a soft bed in danger.

WORD LIST

annoyance

glance

gobble

nap

nibble

rage

slumber

stare

1. Why did the country mouse prefer his own home?

because is that not that dagers.

2. Compare how the two mice slept when they were away from home.

They have a softer bed.
They have 6 types of
cheese.

C Decide which word makes sense in each blank. Write the word on the line.

1. If you just _____ at a painting, you won't really notice all the details; you need to really _____ at a painting to appreciate it. (*glance/stare*)

2. My mother tells me it's not polite to _____ get _____ down my meals, but then my grandmother thinks I don't like her cooking because I only _____ at my food. (*nibble/gobble*)

3. If you _____ several times during the day, you probably won't be tired enough to _____ through the night. (*slumber/nap*)

4. The crowd's _____ at the umpire turned to _____ when he called the runner out. (*annoyance/rage*)

D Write the words from the word list in the boxes in which they fit.

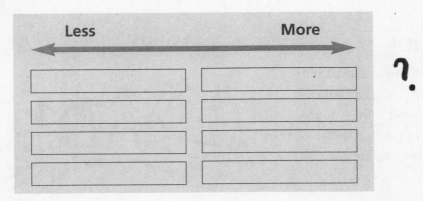

?

OTHER FORMS

annoy

annoyed

annoying

enrage

glanced

napping

nibbling

slumbering

stared

E Complete each sentence with a phrase that makes sense. Note that some other forms of the vocabulary words are used.

1. The twins **annoy** their little sister by _____

_____ .

2. When a baby is **napping**, _____

_____ .

3. If you **nibble** at your meal, _____

_____ .

4. I **glanced** behind me to see if _____

_____ .

5. People **stared** in wonder at _____

_____ .

ENRICHMENT WORDS

Here are two more words mean more or less of the same thing. Both words mean "enough," but one means "more than enough."

1. ample (ăm' pəl) *When there is an* **ample** *amount of something, there is enough of it.* (adjective)

   We had **ample** food for the picnic, so we all ate well.

2. excessive (ĭk sĕs' ĭv) *When there is an* **excessive** *amount of something, there is too much of it.* (adjective)

   Because of the **excessive** number of people, not everyone could get into the concert.

OFF THE PAGE

What **annoys** you? Write at least four sentences about something that annoys you. Include details about why you are annoyed. If you can, use other forms of the word, for example, *annoying* or *annoyed*.

Mosquitoes are annoying!

Review
Lessons 1-4

In this lesson, you will review the words and skills you have learned in the last four lessons. This will help you to remember them when you read and write.

A **MATCHING WORDS AND DEFINITIONS** Choose the word that matches each definition. Write it on the line.

| ~~glance~~ | ~~partner~~ | delectable | sensible | ~~nap~~ |

- 1. showing good judgment _____nap_____
- 2. look quickly _____glance_____
- 3. someone who works with you _____partner_____
- 4. sleep lightly _____sensible_____
- 5. very delicious _____delectable._____

B **USING WORDS IN CONTEXT** Use the words in each list to complete each paragraph.

| fortunate | ~~rude~~ | amusing | ~~gobble~~ | ~~fabulous~~ |

I love to go to the parties that Martin's family has. When his father plays the fiddle, we all say, "That music is just **(1)** _fabulous_ !" When Mr. Hayes plays his fiddle, everyone listens. No one would be **(2)** _rude_ enough to talk. When he is finished, we all take turns telling **(3)** _fortunate_ stories that make people laugh. Then we all **(4)** _amusing_ down a great meal. I feel **(5)** _gobble_ to have a friend like Martin.

| courteous | stare | rage | scarce | annoyance |

A big crowd had gathered to view the sailboat race in the harbor.
Space was **(6)** _____ , but we found a spot with a good
view. We had been waiting two hours when a big cruise boat pulled
in front of us and blocked our view! We asked the boat's captain, in
a **(7)** _____ way, to please move. All he did was
(8) _____ at us. At this point, our **(9)** _____
turned to **(10)** _____ . Then my father used his cell phone
to call the Harbor Master. The Harbor Master found another spot for the
cruise boat, and everyone got to see the sailboat race.

C **WRITING SENTENCES** Choose two of the words on
each line to use in a sentence. You can change the form of the
word if you like. (For example, *courteous* may be changed to
courteously, or *gobble* may be changed to *gobbled*.)

1. **opponent   competent   partner**

   _____

   _____

2. **glance   stare   trustworthy**

   _____

   _____

3. **sensible   nibble   scarce**

   _____

   _____

4. **amusing   enthusiastic   ridiculous**

   _____

   _____

5. **rage   nap   fabulous**

   _____

   _____

D **TEST-TAKING STRATEGIES** An **analogy** compares two pairs of words. In an analogy, both pairs of words are related in the same way.

Strategy: Look at this analogy. Think about how the underlined words in each pair are related.

In is to out as fast is to slow.

The words in each pair are opposites, or **antonyms.** You can put them in a sentence, like this:

In is the opposite of out, and fast is the opposite of slow.

The pairs of words in analogies can be related in other ways. To complete this analogy, think of how the first pair of words is related.

Wonderful is to terrific as tired is to _____ . *(sleepy/awake)*

Wonderful and *terrific* mean about the same, or are **synonyms.** The second pair of words must have the same relationship. Ask yourself, "What means about the same as *tired?*" *Sleepy* means about the same as *tired.*

Directions: Write the word that completes each analogy on the line.

1. Delectable is to tasty as kind is to _____ . *(nasty/nice)*

2. Unlucky is to fortunate as poor is to _____ .
   (rich/homeless)

3. Nap is to slumber as nibble is to _____ . *(food/gobble)*

4. Silly is to ridiculous as happy is to _____ . *(rude/elated)*

5. Wet is to dry as partner is to _____ . *(opponent/friend)*

TEST-TAKING STRATEGIES On a **multiple-choice** test, you have to pick the correct answer out of several choices.

Strategy: Read through each question. Before you make a choice, think of how you would answer the question. Look to see if your answer is one of the choices. If it is, and you are certain it is right, carefully fill in the bubble next to the answer.

Directions: Fill in the bubble next to the best answer to each question.

1. How would you describe a very tasty dessert?
   (A) plentiful   ● gobble   (C) delectable   (D) amusing

2. How would you describe a person on whom you can depend?
   (A) elated   (B) courteous   ● enthusiastic   (D) trustworthy

3. What is another word for extreme anger?
   (A) slumber   ● rage   (C) annoyance   (D) partner

4. Which word is an antonym of *rude?*
   (A) competent   (B) ridiculous   (C) competent   ● courteous

5. Which word is an antonym of *plentiful?*
   (A) fabulous   ● fortunate   (C) scarce   (D) sensible

ENRICHMENT WORDS

Draw a line between each Enrichment Word and its definition.

1. triumph   to end
2. initiate   respect
3. excessive   victory
4. ample   to begin
5. terminate   too much
6. admire   plenty

WORKING WITH WORDS

Skill Lesson
Dictionary skills

The next set of lessons will teach you words that are verbs, adjectives, and adverbs. One way to find out more about these words is to use a **dictionary.** You can use the dictionary to help you work with words to improve your vocabulary.

 USING A DICTIONARY The first thing you need to know about using a dictionary is that the words are arranged in **alphabetical order.** To find a word in the dictionary quickly and easily, it helps to know what part of the dictionary to look in. Think of the dictionary pages in three sections: beginning (A–G), middle (H–P), end (Q–Z). To find the word *billboard*, should you open to the beginning, the middle, or the end of the dictionary? *B* is near the beginning of the alphabet, so you would open near the beginning of the dictionary.

Decide about where you would find each of the words in a dictionary. Write *beginning*, *middle*, or *end*.

1. moth   _middle_
2. zebra   _end_
3. antelope   _beginning_
4. penguin   _middle_
5. dragon   _beginning_

Circle the lists of words that are in alphabetical order, the way they would be in a dictionary. The lists are tricky because the first two letters of the words are the same. Look at the third letter in each word.

LIST 1	LIST 2	LIST 3	LIST 4
hippo	own	one	table
hire	owl	online	taco
his	owe	onion	tadpole

B **READING AN ENTRY** The information given for a word in the dictionary is called an **entry.** Look at the entry below.

```
    ┌─1─┐ ┌─2─┐┌──────────3──────────┐
```
billboard *noun* A large upright board on which advertisements are displayed.
```
    ┌────────4────────┐ ┌────────5────────┐
```
bill•board (bĭl' bôrd') Δ *noun, plural* **billboards**

1. **The word** The entry word is printed in boldface type.

2. **The part of speech** The part of speech is printed in italic type.

3. **The definition** This tells what the word means. If there is more than one definition, they will be numbered. Sometimes a sample sentence follows the definition to show how the word is used.

4. **The pronunciation** A key in the margin and in the front of the dictionary shows how to use these symbols to pronounce the word correctly. (See inside the cover. Syllables are also shown.)

5. **Other forms** Other forms of the word that do not have their own entries may be listed here with their part of speech.

These dictionary entries use the words in sentences. Answer the questions.

subtract *verb* To take away one number or part from another number or a whole; deduct: *If you subtract 4 from 7, you get 3.*
sub•tract (səb trăkt') Δ *verb* **subtracted, subtracting**

1. What part of speech is *subtract?* _____verb_____

2. What is the definition of *subtract?* _to take away one number_

3. What other forms are shown? _part from another Number_

exactly *adverb* **1.** Without any change or mistake; accurately: *Be sure that you follow the recipe exactly.* **2.** In every respect; quite: *You may do exactly as you please.*
ex•act•ly (ĭg săkt' lē) Δ *adverb*

4. What part of speech is *exactly?* _adverb_

5. How many definitions are given for *exactly?* _without any change or mistake._

PRONUNCIATION For each dictionary entry, the **pronunciation** appears in parentheses. The letters and symbols in a word's pronunciation stand for the sounds in the word. A key, such as the one that appears below, explains how to pronounce these letters and symbols. The word is broken into syllables, or parts. The boldfaced part of the word is the accented syllable. In other words, you say it more strongly.

PRONUNCIATION KEY

Sound		Sample Words
ă	as in	pat, laugh
ā		ape, aid, pay
â		air, care, wear
ä		father, koala, yard
b		bib, cabbage
ch		church, stitch
d		deed, mailed, puddle
ĕ		pet, pleasure, any
ē		be, bee, easy, piano
f		fast, fife, off, phrase, rough
ə		ago, silent, lemon, circus

bee (bē)

Look at the pronunciations below and then answer the questions.

abandon (ə **băn'** dən)   **contest** (**kŏn'** tĕst)   **fair** (fâr)

I don't know

1. Is the first *a* in *abandon* pronounced like the *a* in *ape* or the *a* in *ago*?

   ~~bath~~

2. Is the second *a* in *abandon* pronounced like the *a* in *ape* or the *a* in *pat*?

   _____

3. Is the *e* in *contest* pronounced like the *e* in *be* or the *e* in *pet*?

   _____

4. Is the *ai* in *fair* pronounced like the *ai* in *air* or the *ai* in *aid*?

   _____

USING DEFINITIONS Dictionary definitions help you see differences between the meanings of words. Below are pairs of words that are the same part of speech and have similar meanings. Decide which word makes the best sense in each sentence. Write the word on the line.

crouch *verb* To lower the body and keep the arms and legs close; squat.
crouch (krouch) Δ *verb* **crouched, crouching**

bend *verb* To move from an upright position; stoop: *I bent over to pick up the ball.*
bend (bĕnd) Δ *verb* **bent, bending**

1. If you _____ down behind the chair, no one will find you when we play hide and seek.

2. Rick has to _____ down to keep from hitting his head on ceiling of the small plane.

soggy *adjective* Soaked with moisture: *My shoes were soggy after I was out in the rain.*
sog•gy (sô' gē) Δ *adjective* **soggier, soggiest**

damp *adjective* Slightly wet; moist.
damp (dămp) Δ *adjective* **damper, dampest**

3. The clothes were still _____ , even though they had hung outside for several hours.

4. After laying outside in a puddle, the newspaper was very _____ .

LESSON 7

Where the Action Is
verbs

swivel

A Do you remember that verbs are action words? This lesson will teach you eight action verbs to use. As you study the words, think of where and when you do each action.

1. **crouch** (krouch) *When we* **crouch,** *we bend our knees and go down.* (verb)
   When I play hide and seek, I often **crouch** behind a big chair.

2. **delete** (dĭ lēt') *To* **delete** *is to take out or remove.* (verb)
   I think that sentence is too long, so I'm going to **delete** some words.

3. **jeer** (jîr) *To* **jeer** *is to make fun of someone in a rude way.* (verb)
   It's wrong to **jeer** at the mistakes of others.

4. **romp** (rŏmp) *When we* **romp,** *we run and play in a lively way.* (verb)
   I love to **romp** around in the snow with my dog.

5. **snatch** (snăch) *When we* **snatch** *something, we grab it quickly.* (verb)
   Leah tried to **snatch** the glass before it rolled off the table.

6. **swivel** (swĭv' əl) *To* **swivel** *is to turn back and forth.* (verb)
   I like to **swivel** on my mom's desk chair, but it makes me dizzy.

7. **trudge** (trŭj) *When we* **trudge,** *we walk with great effort.* (verb)
   We watched Harry **trudge** up the steep hill pulling the heavy wagon.

8. **tumble** (tŭm' bəl) *To* **tumble** *is to fall or to roll end over end.* (verb)
   We saw Mary **tumble** to the ground when she twisted her ankle.

Draw a line between each vocabulary word and its definition.

1.	trudge	remove
2.	jeer	grab
3.	delete	make fun of
4.	snatch	walk with effort
5.	swivel	bend down
6.	crouch	turn
7.	tumble	run and play
8.	romp	fall

All the boldfaced words in the passage below are action verbs. Read the passage. Then answer the questions that follow.

The Horse that Built America

Did you know that there were no horses in the Americas when Spanish explorers brought them? The Spanish Barb was a horse brought by these explorers. It was developed from a powerful Spanish war horse and the Barbary horse of North Africa. The Spanish Barb was small, but as a war horse, nobody could **jeer** at it. It could run fast, stop instantly, and **swivel** around quickly to avoid an attack. It could **trudge** up and down hills, and it moved smoothly so that a rider would not easily **tumble** to the ground.

Curious and playful, the Spanish Barb liked to **snatch** apples and carrots from people's hands and **romp** with other horses. The Barb's graceful neck and long mane and tail, made it a beautiful horse. But if you **crouched** down to look at its large hoofs, you would understand why it was also known for being a strong mountain climber.

The Spanish Barb helped to build the Americas. These horses were the favorites of many cowboys and Native Americans. They even carried mail for the Pony Express.

However, by 1900, pure Spanish Barbs were hard to find. To help keep this horse from disappearing, a national registry was established. Horses that qualify are put into the first division when they are young. Then, when they are three years old, they can try to qualify for the next division. Even if they don't make it, their names are kept on the first registry and are not **deleted.** Today this registry keeps an important part of our history alive.

1. Give two reasons that the Spanish Barb was a good horse.

   _____

   _____

2. Choose two of the following words to use in one sentence that describes the Spanish Barb: **swivel, romp, trudge, tumble,** or **jeer.**

   _____

crouch

delete

jeer

romp

snatch

swivel

trudge

tumble

C Choose the word that makes sense in the sentence. Write the word on the line.

1. The tired troops had to _____ many miles carrying heavy packs on their backs. *(jeer/trudge)*

2. Josh had to _____ down and shine a flashlight under the porch to see the kittens. *(swivel/crouch)*

3. I'm going to _____ all the computer files I don't need anymore. *(delete/tumble)*

4. Jenna tried to _____ her diary as her brother waved it in the air. *(romp/snatch)*

5. Someone should tell Jack that if he isn't careful he'll _____ down the hill. *(crouch/tumble)*

D Complete the crossword puzzle, using words from the word list.

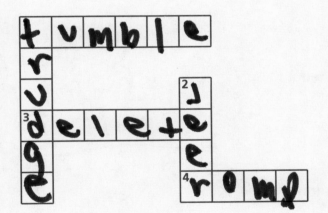

Across
1. turn back and forth
3. roll end over end
4. run and play

Down
1. grab
2. make fun of

OTHER FORMS

crouching
deleting
jeering
romping
snatching
swiveling
trudging
tumbling

E Complete each sentence with a phrase that makes sense. Note that some other forms of the vocabulary words are used.

1. **Crouching** down and looking behind the sofa, I could see

_____ .

2. The way I **delete** a sentence from my paper is to _____

_____ .

3. When you are **trudging** up a hill, _____

_____ .

4. You might **snatch** something if _____

_____ .

5. The crowd was **jeering** because _____

_____ .

ENRICHMENT WORDS

Here are two more words that express action. Have you ever sprinted or strolled?

1. **sprint** (sprĭnt) *When we **sprint**, we run very fast for a short time.* (verb)

   To pass the other runner I **sprinted** for a few seconds.

2. **stroll** (strōl) *To **stroll** is to walk slowly.* (verb)

   We like to **stroll** down Main Street, stopping to look in the shop windows.

OFF THE PAGE

Choose one verb you have learned and think of three situations in which you or others would do this action. Then draw a picture and write a sentence for each situation. For example, you might trudge up a hill, across a shallow stream, and while carrying a heavy backpack.

stroll

Strong Words
adjectives

diminutive

A If you haven't had enough sleep, you might be tired. But, if you are *very* tired, you are weary. All the adjectives below describe something in a strong way.

1. **diminutive** (dĭ mĭn' yə tĭv) *Something that is* **diminutive** *is very small.* (adjective)
The **diminutive** Chihuahua is the smallest breed of dog in the world.

2. **immense** (ĭ mĕns') *Something that is* **immense** *is very large.* (adjective)
The **immense** General Sherman sequoia tree stands 272 feet tall.

3. **prominent** (prŏm' ə nənt) *Someone or something* **prominent** *is well known and important.* (adjective).
The president of the United States is a **prominent** person in world politics.

4. **swift** (swĭft) *Something that is* **swift** *is very fast.* (adjective)
The firefighters' **swift** arrival helped to keep the fire from spreading.

5. **tardy** (tär' dē) *Someone who is* **tardy** *is late.* (adjective)
When the school bus had a flat tire, the children were **tardy** for school.

6. **unimportant** (ŭn' ĭm pôr' tnt) *Something* **unimportant** *is meaningless or not important.* (adjective)
Losing my bike in the flood seemed **unimportant** when I found out that my friend's house had washed away.

7. **urgent** (ûr' jənt) *Something* **urgent** *is very important and needs to be done quickly.* (adjective)
When Caroline was hurt on the playground, the school nurse made an **urgent** call to her mother at work.

8. **weary** (wîr' ē) *People who are* **weary** *are very tired.* (adjective)
The **weary** children went straight to bed when they returned from their long hike.

Draw a line between each vocabulary word and its definition.

1. swift	well-known
2. unimportant	very fast
3. prominent	late
4. tardy	not important
5. diminutive	needs to be done fast
6. weary	very large
7. immense	very tired
8. urgent	very small

All of the boldfaced words in the passage below are adjectives. Read the passage. Then do the exercises that follow.

Operation Smile

José Bravo was born in Brazil with a cleft palate and other problems that gave his face an unusual appearance. Because of this, people did not take good care of him. But, thanks to Operation Smile, he has received medical help and has even found a loving family.

Operation Smile gives medical help to poor children who need surgery on their faces. Doctors say they help children "one smile at a time." One may seem like an **unimportant** number, but since 1982, Operation Smile has helped an **immense** number of children—over 50,000! Many different groups and **prominent** people, such as actress Goldie Hawn, help to raise money for the children's treatment.

Operation Smile helped José Bravo find a new smile and a new family. When he was one year old, he came to the United States for an operation on  his face. The Besselman family helped to care for him. Mrs. Besselman went to the hospital every day. Nurses told her that José  watched the door until she arrived, so she tried not to be **tardy.**

Doctors had hoped José would have a **swift** recovery from surgery, but he became very sick. One day Mrs. Besselman received an **urgent** call saying he might die. Mrs. Besselman was also ill, and she was too **weary** to go. Instead, Mr. Besselman went.

Doctors asked Mr. Besselman to hold José. Suddenly, José squeezed Mr. Besselman's finger with his **diminutive** hand. From that moment, José started to recover. Later, the Besselmans adopted José.

Many children such as José owe their happy faces to Operation Smile. This organization is doing something that should make us all smile!

1. In what way does Operation Smile help children?

_____

_____

2. What made the phone call to Mrs. Bessleman urgent?

_____

_____

C Choose the word that makes sense in the sentence. Write the word on the line.

1. There's an _____ need for medical supplies in the disaster area. *(unimportant/urgent)*

2. The _____ cat was able to run faster than the big dog. *(swift/weary)*

3. Playing soccer after school made me _____ for band practice. *(prominent/tardy)*

4. The _____ print in the dictionary is hard to read. *(diminutive/weary)*

5. After the storm, an _____ pile of snow blocked the driveway. *(swift/immense)*

D Write the word from the word list that means the same as the words in each list.

1. not important, meaningless, insignificant, _____

2. important, notable, well known, _____

3. fast, quick, speedy, _____

4. tired, worn out, drained, _____

5. large, huge, enormous, _____

OTHER FORMS

immensely

prominently

swiftly

swiftness

tardiness

urgently

wearily

weariness

E Complete each sentence with a phrase that makes sense. Note that some other forms of the vocabulary words are used.

1. An example of something **diminutive** is _____

_____ .

2. If you need something **urgently,** _____

_____ .

3. A good time to move **swiftly** is _____

_____ .

4. When you are **tardy,** _____

_____ .

5. Displayed **prominently** in front of the store was _____

_____ .

ENRICHMENT WORDS

Here are two more adjectives. *Skimpy* describes an amount or size. *Crucial* describes how important something is.

1. **skimpy** (skĭm′ pē) *A* **skimpy** *amount is not enough.* (adjective)

   After the **skimpy** meal, we were still hungry.

2. **crucial** (krōo′ shəl) *Something* **crucial** *is so important that it is necessary.* (adjective)

   Air is **crucial** to human beings.

OFF THE PAGE

Write four sentences about what might cause someone to be **weary.** How would a weary person act? What might that person look like?

a skimpy meal

Telling How
adverbs

I rode my bike . . .
tirelessly
happily
dreadfully

A When you want to tell how something is done, use an adverb. Adverbs describe verbs, adjectives, and other adverbs. The words below are adverbs. Like most adverbs, they end in -ly.

1. **dreadfully** (drĕd' fə lē) **Dreadfully** *means very badly, terribly, or unpleasantly.* (adverb)
Mrs. Sanchez put a low grade on the **dreadfully** written paper.

2. **happily** (hăp' ə lē) *Something done* **happily** *is done with joy or in a happy way.* (adverb)
Avi smiled **happily** when he saw the *A* on his paper.

3. **hastily** (hā' stə lē) **Hastily** *means done in a quick way, often without care.* (adverb)
Cassandra rushed off so **hastily** that she forgot her coat.

4. **repeatedly** (rĭ pē' təd lē) *Something done* **repeatedly** *is done over and over.* (adverb)
My mom **repeatedly** reminds me to look both ways before I cross the street.

5. **sadly** (săd' lē) **Sadly** *means in a sad way; with sorrow.* (adverb)
Andrea's parents told her **sadly** that their new apartment building doesn't allow pets.

6. **tirelessly** (tīr' lĭs lē) *Something done* **tirelessly** *is done for a long time, without getting tired.* (adverb)
Mrs. Goldberg worked **tirelessly** for two weeks on the huge school picnic.

7. **usefully** (yōos' fə lē) **Usefully** *means in a helpful or useful way.* (adverb)
Bob spent his time in the after-school program **usefully,** by doing his homework.

8. **uselessly** (yōos' lĕs lē) **Uselessly** *means in a way that is not helpful.* (adverb)
We spent our time **uselessly** arguing instead of making plans to see a movie.

Draw a line between each vocabulary word and its definition.

1. hastily   in a tireless way
2. usefully   in a quick way
3. happily   in a helpful way
4. tirelessly   in a happy way
5. repeatedly   in a sad way
6. uselessly   in a useless way
7. sadly   very badly
8. dreadfully   over and over

All the boldfaced words in the passage below are adverbs.
Read the passage. Then answer the questions that follow.

Hiccups in Us and on the Internet

Everybody has had them. Most of the time we don't know why or how to get rid of them. **Happily** they almost always go away by themselves. What are they? Why, hiccups, of course.

What is a hiccup? It is a sudden, quick catching of the breath, made when you don't breathe normally, and the space between the two vocal cords in your throat closes. Doctors think hiccups may come from eating too **hastily** or from taking in too much air. Most people don't hiccup just once. Instead, they do it **repeatedly** for a few minutes. Hiccups usually don't last much longer than that.

Because the hiccups can be **dreadfully** uncomfortable, people have searched **tirelessly** for a cure. Some of the stranger cures are holding peanut butter on the end of your tongue or eating a tablespoon of brown or white sugar. People have **uselessly** rubbed their bellies, pulled hard on their tongues, or been tickled by friends. None of these activities seems to stop the hiccups. More **usefully,** doctors suggest that you try to hold your breath for as long as you can. This helps to put more carbon dioxide in your body and seems to stop the hiccups. **Sadly,** however, no one knows of a cure that works all the time.

The term "hiccup" is now also used to refer to computer problems. Web sites on the Internet sometimes have short-term problems for what seems like no reason. These problems have come to be known as "hiccups." Like the real hiccups, they often just go away by themselves.

1. In what two ways do Internet hiccups remind you of real hiccups?

_____

_____

2. Circle the word in the passage that describes how people have tried to cure their hiccups. What does this word tell you about the cures?

_____

_____

WORD LIST

dreadfully   10

happily   7

hastily

repeatedly •

sadly   •

tirelessly •

usefully

uselessly   9.

C Choose the word that best describes the underlined verb in each sentence. Write the word on the line.

1. My dog <u>barks</u> _____ when he's left alone for several hours. *(dreadfully/happily)*

2. The broken TV <u>sits</u> _____ in the living room. *(sadly/uselessly)*

3. Mom _____ <u>cleaned</u> up the strawberry jam from the white carpet. *(happily/hastily)*

4. Leon _____ <u>said</u> his last good-byes to his old friends. *(usefully/sadly)*

5. We're now <u>settled</u> _____ in our wonderful new home. *(repeatedly/happily)*

D Complete the crossword puzzle, using words from the word list.

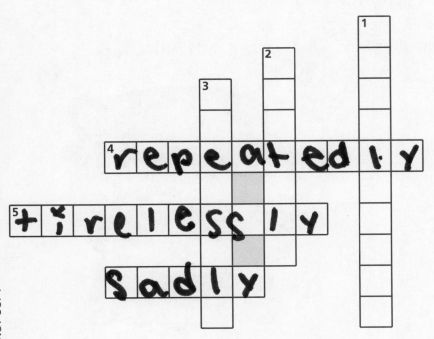

Across

4. again and again ~ repeatedly
5. very badly ~ tirelessly
6. not happily ~ sadly

Down

1. without tiring ~
2. quickly ~
3. helpfully ~

4 repeatedly
5 tirelessly
sadly

dreadful
happy
hasty
repeat
sad
tireless
useful
useless

E Complete each sentence with a phrase that makes sense. Note that other forms of some vocabulary words are used.

1. If you are **dreadfully** late, _____

_____ .

2. If you do something **hastily,** _____

_____ .

3. When you spend time **usefully,** _____

_____ .

4. A **happy** face _____

_____ .

5. When you feel **sad,** _____

_____ .

ENRICHMENT WORDS

Here are two more adverbs that tell how something is done.

1. **contentedly** (kən tĕn' tĭd lē) **Contentedly** *means in a satisfied or contented way.* (adverb)

   The tiny kitten purred **contentedly** when we petted her.

2. **exceedingly** (ĭk sē' dĭng lē) **Exceedingly** *means very.* (adverb)

   It is **exceedingly** important to wear a seat belt when riding in a car.

OFF THE PAGE

Describe two ways people spend time **usefully.** Then describe two ways that people spend time **uselessly.**

The kitten purred contentedly.

Review
Lessons 6-9

In this lesson, you will review the words and skills you have learned in the last four lessons. This will help you to remember them when you read and write.

A **MATCHING WORDS AND DEFINITIONS**
Write the word that matches each definition.

| prominent | tardy | repeatedly | weary | crouch | delete |

1. over and over _____
2. important _____
3. to lower the body by bending the knees _____
4. late _____
5. very tired _____
6. take away _____

B **USING WORDS IN CONTEXT** Use the words in 38the lists to complete the two paragraphs. Use the part of speech to help you fill in each blank.

| diminutive | crouched | swift | snatched | romp |

Sylvia watched the four kittens **(1)** _____ (verb) and play together and wondered how she would ever choose one to take home. She began to notice that the **(2)** _____ (adjective) black kitten was the most playful. It **(3)** _____ (verb) low in the grass and **(4)** _____ (verb) the other kittens' tails. Then it made a **(5)** _____ (adjective) escape to the safety of Sylvia's lap. Sylvia knew that her choice had been made for her.

trudged   tardy   weary   dreadfully   happily

Ali was **(6)** _____ (adverb) lost in the woods and his growling stomach told him that he was **(7)** _____ (adjective) for dinner. With **(8)** _____ (adjective) steps, he **(9)** _____ (verb) on, looking for the path back to the campsite. Suddenly, he stepped into a clearing, and there it was. **(10)** _____ (adverb) , he recognized his family's tent. "You're late," said his mother, as she dished up the most delicious dinner Ali had ever eaten.

C **WRITING SENTENCES** Choose two of the words on each line to use in a sentence. You can change the form of the word if you like. (For example, *tirelessly* may be changed to *tireless* or *jeer* may be changed to *jeered*.)

1. **jeer   tirelessly   tumble**

   _____

   _____

2. **immense   hastily   swivel**

   _____

   _____

3. **unimportant   sadly   urgent**

   _____

   _____

4. **weary   usefully   uselessly**

   _____

   _____

5. **prominent   delete   swift**

   _____

   _____

TEST-TAKING STRATEGIES In an **analogy,** both pairs of words are related in the same way. In Lesson 5, you learned about synonyms and antonyms in analogies. In this lesson, you'll learn about analogies that describe.

Strategy: Look at this analogy. Think about how each pair of underlined words are related.

Quickly is to run as neatly is to write.

The first word in each pair word describes how something is done. This word is an adverb. The other word is the action (verb). Each pair has an adverb followed by an verb. You can put them in a sentence, like this:

Quickly tells how you can run, and neatly tells how you can write.

Here's an example with an adjective followed by a noun.

Green is to leaves as blue is to sky.

Directions: Write the word that completes each analogy on the line. The analogies may be synonyms, antonyms, or analogies that describe.

1. Happily is to smile as sadly is to _____ . *(frown/laugh)*

2. Urgent is to important as terribly is to _____ . *(dreadfully/usefully)*

3. Diminutive is to mouse as immense is to _____ . *(large/elephant)*

4. Romp is to play as trudge is to _____ . *(walk/run)*

5. Early is to tardy as slowly is to _____ . *(uselessly/hastily)*

Name

Date

 TEST-TAKING STRATEGIES On a **multiple-choice** test, you have to pick the correct answer out of several choices. Usually two or three of the answers seem like good choices, but only one answer is correct.

Strategy: Read through each question and all the answer choices. If there are any choices that you know are wrong, skip them. Then study the rest of the choices to see which one makes the best sense. Make sure you fill in the bubble completely.

Directions: Fill in the bubble next to the best answer to each question.

1. Which word is an adverb that describes something done over and over?

   (A) usefully   (B) trudge   (C) hastily   (D) repeatedly

2. Which word is a verb that describes a turning motion?

   (A) swivel   (B) jeer   (C) crouch   (D) tirelessly

3. Which word is an adjective that describes a very important person?

   (A) insignificant   (B) sadly   (C) prominent   (D) weary

4. What is a word that is a synonym for *grab?*

   (A) snatch   (B) tumble   (C) romp   (D) delete

5. Which of the following is an antonym of *slow?*

   (A) tardy   (B) swift   (C) weary   (D) unimportant

ENRICHMENT WORDS

Draw a line between each Enrichment Word and its definition.

1. skimpy   run fast for a short time
2. exceedingly   necessary
3. contentedly   very
4. sprint   not enough
5. stroll   in a satisfied way
6. crucial   walk slowly

THINKING WITH WORDS

Skill Lesson
using context

In your school lessons and in your own reading, you will come across lots of new words in different subject areas. In this lesson, you will learn ways to figure out the meanings of new words.

A **SENTENCE CONTEXT** One way to figure out the meaning of a new word is to think about the meaning of what you are reading. You can look for clues in the sentences around an unknown word. These sentences are called the **context.** Suppose you are reading a history book and you come across these sentences:

> The king often traveled with his nobles and servants from one castle to another. The people along the way had to give food and rooms to sleep in to the king and his **retinue.**

What does the word **retinue** mean? You know that the king is traveling with his nobles and servants. You also know that the people were expected to give food and rooms to the king. Common sense tells you that they would be expected to provide the same for the people who traveled with the king—his nobles and servants. You can figure out, then, that **retinue** means the nobles and servants traveling with the king.

the king and his retinue

Here are some examples for you to try. Write the letter of the word or phrase that means about the same as the boldfaced word.

1. The queen didn't like the way her servants behaved, so she **banished** them from the palace. _____

   A. welcomed   **B.** forced   **C.** hired

2. The king issued a **proclamation** that taxes would be raised for everyone. _____

   A. announcement   **B.** question   **C.** hope

3. Scientists worked quickly to find a cure that could stop the spread of the **epidemic.** _____

   A. party   **B.** disease   **C.** idea

4. Cleaning surfaces with **disinfectant** helps to cut down the spread of disease. _____

   A. something that destroys water   **B.** something that destroys food
   C. something that destroys germs

5. We stayed away from the wood because it was crawling with **vermin.** _____

   A. rats   **B.** flowers   **C.** broken glass

B **SUBSTITUTION CONTEXT CLUES** Sometimes you can check the meaning of a new word by putting a familiar word or phrase in its place. This is called a **substitution** clue. Usually, the word or phrase you substitute will be a rough definition for the unknown word.

Choose the best substitute for the boldfaced word in each sentence. Circle your answer. The first one is done for you.

1. The king had his guards **escort** him home to his castle to keep him safe. (*go along with*/*play a game with*)

2. The colorful costumes and shiny instruments in the parade were quite a **spectacle.** (*eyeglasses/marvelous sight*)

3. No one wanted to breathe when they passed the town dump because of the terrible **odor** of rotting garbage. (*sight/smell*)

4. Pilots must stay **alert** at all times so that they will fly the planes safely. (*awake/happy*)

5. You can tell that wolves are in the **canine** family because they look a lot like dogs. (*dogs/cats*)

6. The scientist was very **methodical** about the way she did her research, keeping careful, complete records on everything. (*orderly/messy*)

C **DEFINING CONTEXT CLUES** Writers sometimes include the meaning of an unfamiliar word right in the sentence. Looking in the text for a **definition** is another way to figure out the meaning of a word. This is a **defining** clue.

Underline the words in each sentence that tell you the meaning of the boldfaced word. Then write the word's definition.

1. Mrs. Johnson was so interested in weaving that she bought a **loom,** a large frame on which yarn is woven to make cloth.

   A loom is ___a large frame on which yarn is woven to make cloth___ .

2. I **feigned,** or pretended, sickness so that I wouldn't have to go to school to take the test.

   Feigned means _____ .

3. We watched the **sanderlings,** small shore birds, run quickly along the edge of the ocean, looking for food.

   Sanderlings are _____ .

4. The new curtain for the stage is dark purplish red, or **maroon.**

   Maroon is _____ .

5. Outside the restaurant, the bright **neon** light—a light lit by an odorless, colorless gas—flashed a colorful "Open."

   Neon is _____ .

6. Until the American Revolution, the colonies were ruled by a **monarch,** who was the king of England.

   A monarch is _____ .

sanderlings

D **CONTEXT AND DICTIONARY** There are words in English that have more than one meaning. The only way you can tell which meaning is meant in your reading is by using the context. Read the dictionary entries below. Then read each sentence and decide which meaning of the word is meant. Write the number of the definition on the line.

limb *noun* **1.** A paired and jointed animal part, such as a leg, arm, wing, or flipper. **2.** One of the larger branches of a tree.
limb (lĭm) Δ *noun, plural* **limbs**

1. The strong winds of the hurricane sent a huge **limb** crashing onto our roof. _____

2. Dad hung our tire swing from the **limb**. _____

3. The young deer had trouble walking with an injured **limb**. _____

beam *noun* **1.** A long, sturdy piece of wood or metal used in building as a horizontal support for floors or ceilings. **2.** A ray of light, as from a flashlight or the sun.
beam (bēm) Δ *noun, plural* **beams**

1. "This **beam** supports the roof," said the carpenter. _____

2. We aimed the **beam** toward the noise and found that a raccoon was trying to open our garbage can. _____

3. Dusty the cat curled up in a **beam** of sunlight. _____

beam of light

LESSON 12

Royal Matters words from social studies and literature

jester

A Perhaps you have heard of the Queen of Great Britain or the King of Spain. Or you may have read tales about princes and princesses who lived long ago. The words you learn here will be useful in social studies and literature.

1. **court** (kôrt) *A* **court** *is the place where a ruler lives or the people who follow a ruler.* (noun)
Everyone in the king's **court** was very loyal to him.

2. **debt** (dĕt) *A* **debt** *is something that you owe; to be in debt is to owe something.* (noun)
The man owed a **debt** to the king who had lent him money.

3. **emperor** (ĕm' pər ər) *An* **emperor** *is a man who rules a large country or group of countries called an empire.* (noun)
At one time, the **emperor** of Austria ruled over Austria, Hungary, and part of Poland.

4. **escort** (ĕs' kôrt') *When we* **escort** *someone, we go with them to protect them or to show respect.* (verb)
Three guards were asked to **escort** the visiting prince into the palace.

5. **jester** (jĕs' tər) *A* **jester** *was a person whose job it was to entertain a ruler.* (noun)
The **jester** knew a lot of funny stories.

6. **procession** (prə sĕsh' ən) *A* **procession** *is a group of people or things moving in a line.* (noun)
A long **procession** followed the queen to the place she would be crowned.

7. **royal** (roi' əl) *Something* **royal** *describes a king, queen, prince, or princess.* (adjective)
A king, a queen, and two princesses were the members of the **royal** family.

8. **spectacle** (spek' tə kəl) *A* **spectacle** *is a large or unusual public show.* (noun)
With its colorful costumes, floats, and music, the Mummer's parade in Philadelphia is quite a **spectacle.**

Draw a line from each word to its definition.

1. court   large public show
2. emperor   go with someone
3. spectacle   where a ruler lives
4. escort   ruler

All the boldfaced words in the Hans Christian Andersen tale have to do with rulers and their courts. Read the passage. Then answer the questions that follow.

The Emperor's New Clothes

One day, two men came to an **emperor** and said, "We are tailors who sew **royal** clothes from magical cloth. This cloth can be seen only by people who do their jobs well. To people who do not do their jobs well, the clothes will be invisible." The emperor immediately ordered clothes from the men.

Actually, there was no cloth at all. The men simply pretended to be making clothes. They also asked for money from the emperor. They said that making the clothes was so expensive that they were going into **debt.** Of course, the emperor gave them the money.

The emperor was curious, so he went to see the tailors. Imagine his horror when the clothes were invisible to him!

"I must be a bad emperor!" he thought. But he told the men that the clothes were wonderful.

Next the emperor sent his oldest daughter to see the clothes. The emperor asked her teacher to **escort** her. Of course, neither one could see the clothes. But they told each other how beautiful they were.

Finally, the **jester** went to see the clothes. "I must make terrible jokes," he thought, "for I cannot see the clothes." But when he returned to the **court,** he told the emperor the clothes were very fine.

At last the clothes were ready. The emperor led a great **procession** to show them off. It was quite a **spectacle,** because the emperor marched in his underwear. The people cheered and shouted anyway, for they were afraid to admit they did not see the clothes.

Suddenly one little child shouted, "This is a trick. The emperor has no clothes!" And so a small child proved that he was more honest than anyone in the royal court.

WORD LIST

court

debt

emperor

escort

jester

procession

royal

spectacle

1. What trick did the tailors play? Why do you think they did it?

_____

_____

2. What made the procession such a spectacle?

_____

_____

C Choose the word that best completes each sentence. Write it on the line.

1. Hirohito was the _____ of Japan for many years in the 1900s. *(emperor/debt)*

2. Princess Diana was a most popular member of Britain's _____ family. *(spectacle/royal)*

3. Columbus went to the _____ of King Ferdinand and Queen Isabella in Spain to ask for money to pay for his trip. *(procession/court)*

4. Whenever the queen goes out in public, the guards _____ her. *(court/escort)*

D The underlined words in each sentence define one of the words in the word list. Write the word on the line.

1. The king thought that the _____, <u>the person who made jokes to amuse him</u>, wasn't funny enough.

2. When you have a big <u>amount that you owe to someone</u>, or _____, it's best to pay it as soon as possible.

3. The fireworks display over the water should be quite a _____, or <u>large public show</u>.

4. A horse-drawn carriage led the _____, or <u>line of people moving along</u>, to the palace.

OTHER FORMS

| debtor |
| empire |
| empress |
| jest |
| royalty |
| spectacular |

E Complete each sentence with a phrase that makes sense. Note that some other forms of the vocabulary words have been used.

1. Something that is **spectacular** is _____

_____ .

2. If you say something in **jest**, _____

_____ .

3. If you are in **debt**, _____

_____ .

4. Famous people usually have an **escort** with them because _____

_____ .

5. An **empress** is _____

_____ .

ENRICHMENT WORDS

Here are two more words that you can use to talk about royal matters.

1. **ambassador** (ăm băs' ə dər) *An* **ambassador** *is a high official who represents his or her country in another country.* (noun)

   The queen appointed an **ambassador** to Israel.

2. **etiquette** (ĕt' ĭ kĭt) **Etiquette** *refers to the rules of proper and polite behavior.* (noun)

   According to court **etiquette,** all visitors to the queen should kneel.

OFF THE PAGE

If you were made **court jester,** tell what you would do to amuse the **royal** family so you could keep your job. Include sample jokes or tricks. Your description should be in a paragraph of at least four sentences. Be sure to include the words *court*, *jester*, and *royal*.

LESSON 13

Lab Notes
words from science

A Science has changed our lives over the last 100 years. We have healthier food, cleaner water, and less disease. We have traveled to the moon and used the telephone and the Internet to send instant messages. The words in this lesson will help you to read and write about scientific discoveries.

1. **alert** (ə lûrt') *An* **alert** *person is wide awake and quick to notice things.* (adjective)
Airplane pilots need to stay **alert** at all times.

2. **analyze** (ăn' ə līz') *When we* **analyze** *something, we study it by breaking it into parts.* (verb)
When we **analyze** light waves, we find that they contain many different colors.

3. **biologist** (bī ŏl' ə jĭst) *A* **biologist** *is a scientist who studies living things, such as plants or animals, and life processes.* (noun)
Biologist Randy Wells studies dolphins who live in the Gulf of Mexico.

4. **experiment** (ĭk spĕr' ə mĕnt') *An* **experiment** *is a scientific test to find out or prove something.* (noun)
The scientist ran an **experiment** to see which medicine would kill the germs.

5. **laboratory** (lăb' rə tôr' ē) *A* **laboratory** *is a place equipped for doing scientific research and experiments.* (noun)
As a teenager, astronaut May Jemison worked in a hospital **laboratory.**

6. **methodical** (mə thŏd' ĭ kəl) *Something done in a* **methodical** *way is done in a systematic and orderly way.* (adjective)
Hospital workers need to be **methodical** when they test blood samples.

7. **odor** (ō' dər) *An* **odor** *is a smell.* (noun)
A skunk gives off an unpleasant **odor** when it is scared or in danger.

8. **particular** (pər tĭk' yə lər) *Someone who is* **particular** *is very careful, pays close attention, and chooses carefully.* (adjective)
My dad is **particular** about eating only low-fat foods.

Draw a line between each vocabulary word and its definition.

1. experiment		smell
2. particular		wide awake
3. alert		scientific test
4. odor		careful

All the boldfaced words in the passage below relate to science. Read the passage. Then answer the questions that follow.

Penicillin: The Accidental Miracle

During World War I, many British soldiers were dying from infections caused by bacteria. At that time, **biologists** knew that antiseptics killed bacteria, but they also killed healthy blood cells. Alexander Fleming, a British doctor, was sent to a battlefield hospital **laboratory** to try to find a way to cure these infections. He wondered if something else could be found to kill bacteria.

After the war, Dr. Fleming continued to do **experiments** on bacteria. Although he was a good scientist who made many important discoveries, Fleming was not known for being very **particular** in his methods. One day in 1928, by accident, he left the cover off one dish of bacteria. Later, he saw that a green mold had formed in this dish. Strangely, the bacteria around the mold had died.

Dr. Fleming was **alert** enough not to throw the dish away. Instead, he **analyzed** the mold that killed the bacteria. If the mold could kill this bacteria, perhaps it could be used to fight infections. Dr. Fleming ran **methodical** tests to see the effects of the bacteria on living things. He found that the mold destroyed bacteria, but

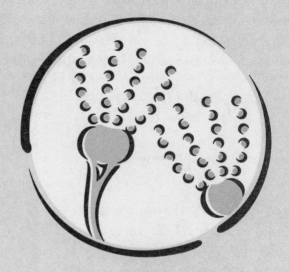

did not harm human tissues. The mold, called *Penicillium notatum*, was a common green mold, with an **odor** like moldy bread. In 1929 Fleming named his discovery penicillin.

However, Fleming was unable to produce penicillin in a way that was pure enough to be used on humans. Finally, when World War II broke out, two other scientists, Sir Howard Florey and Ernst Chain, came up with a way to produce a pure form of the mold.

Today penicillin is used to cure throat infections, pneumonia, and spinal meningitis. Dr. Fleming's accident has helped millions of people throughout the world.

WORD LIST

alert

analyze

biologist

experiment

laboratory

methodical

odor

particular

1. What is the most surprising thing you learned about penicillin? Explain.

_____

_____

2. What made Dr. Fleming a good researcher? What words tell you this?

_____

_____

C Choose the word that best completes each sentence. Write it on the line.

1. I'm going to conduct an _____ to try to prove that too much water is worse for plants than too little water. *(alert/experiment)*

2. The high school science _____ needs better equipment. *(particular/laboratory)*

3. Kate will make a good scientist because she is very _____. *(methodical/analyze)*

4. The foul _____ was coming from a huge pile of garbage outside the window. *(biologist/odor)*

5. A wildlife biologist needs to be _____ to every change in an animal's habitat. *(alert/methodical)*

D Choose the word from the word list that means about the same as each group of words below. Write the word on the line.

1. take apart, examine, study, _____

2. careful, slow, orderly, _____

3. smell, fragrance, aroma, _____

4. fussy, choosing carefully, attentive, _____

5. awake, prepared for, ready, _____

OTHER FORMS

alertness

analysis

biology

experimental

method

methodically

odorous

particularly

E Complete each sentence with a phrase that makes sense. Note that some other forms of the vocabulary words have been used.

1. A good reason to do an **analysis** is _____ _____ .

2. Something **experimental** is _____ _____ .

3. In a **laboratory** you might find _____ _____ .

4. It's good to be **methodical** when _____ _____ .

5. In a **biology** class, you might study _____ _____ .

ENRICHMENT WORDS

Here are two more words that you might see in books about science.

1. **bacteria** (băk tîr' ē ∂) **Bacteria** *are one-celled living organisms that are shaped like rods, spirals, or curves.* (noun, plural)
Some **bacteria** cause disease, but others help us digest food.

2. **mold** (mōld) **Mold** *is a type of fungus that forms a fuzzy coating on the surface of damp or rotting things.* (noun)
Mold is growing on the cheese that I forgot to put in the refrigerator.

OFF THE PAGE

Find something in or around school or your home and analyze it. Your analysis should be methodical. Describe the object, giving at least four details.

Animal Talk
more words from science

canine? feline?

A Should you describe a dog as a *carnivore, herbivore, canine,* or *feline*? If you're not sure, you can find out in this lesson. You will learn scientific words to describe the world's many types of animals.

1. **canine** (kā' nīn) *A* **canine** *is a member of the dog family; dogs, foxes, wolves, and coyotes are canines.* (noun)
A **canine** has sharp, pointed teeth on both upper and lower jaws.

2. **carnivore** (kär' nĭ vôr') *A* **carnivore** *is an animal that eats meat.* (noun)
The tiger is an example of an animal that is a **carnivore.**

3. **domesticated** (də měs' tĭ kāt' əd) *A* **domesticated** *animal has been tamed and trained to live with and be of use to humans.* (adjective)
Pigs, cows, and chickens are all **domesticated** animals.

4. **feline** (fē' līn') *A* **feline** *is a member of the cat family; lions, tigers, leopards, and house cats are felines.* (noun)
A **feline** has soft fur, sharp claws, whiskers, and, often, a long tail.

5. **herbivore** (hûr' bə vôr') *A* **herbivore** *is an animal that eats only plants.* (noun)
The mighty elephant is a **herbivore.**

6. **primitive** (prĭm' ĭ tĭv) *Something that is* **primitive** *is in an early stage or has a simple form.* (adjective)
Horseshoe crabs are **primitive** animals that have not changed for millions of years.

7. **reptilian** (rĕp tĭl' ē ən) **Reptilian** *describes a reptile, such as a snake, turtle, or lizard.* (adjective)
Scales are a **reptilian** feature that keeps snakes from becoming too dry.

8. **vertebrate** (vûr' tə brĭt) *A* **vertebrate** *is an animal with a backbone, such as a fish, amphibian, reptile, bird, or mammal.* (noun)
A **vertebrate** has its skeleton inside its body.

Draw a line from each word to its definition.

1. carnivore   plant-eating animal
2. feline   member of the dog family
3. herbivore   animal that eats meat
4. canine   member of the cat family
5. reptilian   animal with a backbone
6. vertebrate   describes a snake

All the boldfaced words in the passage below are related to
animals. Read the passage. Then answer the questions that follow.

Pets Have Been Our Friends for Thousands of Years

Over eleven thousand years ago, groups of **canines** gathered near the campfires of **primitive** human beings. These **carnivores** were probably looking for leftover meat, very much like dogs by the dinner table today. Perhaps a child began to feed one friendly animal. In this way, wild dogs became **domesticated** into pets.

People found that dogs were useful. The dog's very fine sense of smell helped humans hunt animals for food. Dogs also could hear very well, so they warned humans of danger. Today, dogs still help humans hunt and guard homes.

The ancient Egyptians made pets out of the common household cat about 3,500 years ago. Even before they kept cats as pets, the Egyptians worshipped **felines.** Egyptians even built temples to honor cats.

Although today cats and dogs are most popular, humans have made pets of many different animals. Some people keep **reptilian** pets such as snakes. Of course, owners must be very careful to care for these pets well and to guard against possible dangers.

Most people own pets that are **vertebrates,** but there are other types of pets. People can even keep insects such as the walking stick. This insect, a cousin of the grasshopper, is about four inches long and does not fly. It is a **herbivore** that eats lettuce. Although the insect may not be as loyal as a dog, its owner does not have to walk it!

1. What was the first domesticated animal? Give two ways in which this
   pet served human beings.

   _____

   _____

2. Which of the following types of animals would make the most
   interesting pet: *feline, herbivore, reptilian, canine?* Explain your choice.

   _____

   _____

WORD LIST

canine

carnivore

domesticated

feline

herbivore

primitive

reptilian

vertebrate

C Choose the word that best completes each sentence. Write it on the line.

1. The _____ paintings were put on the cave walls thousands of years ago. *(primitive/domesticated)*

2. A hungry _____ would not eat vegetables from the garden. *(reptilian/carnivore)*

3. The _____ cat is much smaller than most types of wild cats. *(domesticated/reptilian)*

4. A cow, because it eats grass, is an example of a _____. *(feline/herbivore)*

5. An animal that slinks around like a snake might be described as _____. *(canine/reptilian)*

D Write the words below in the column of the chart in which they fit best.

snake   turtle   tiger   wolf   lizard   cougar
coyote   alligator   cat   lion   fox   dog

Canine	Reptilian	Feline

reptilian

OTHER FORMS

carnivorous

domestic

domesticated

herbivorous

primitively

reptile

E Complete each sentence with a phrase that makes sense. Note that some other forms of the vocabulary words have been used.

1. A **herbivorous** animal might eat _____

_____ .

2. My favorite **domesticated** animal is _____

because _____ .

3. The best thing about **felines** is _____

_____ .

4. One thing about **carnivorous** animals is _____

_____ .

5. Some people prefer not to have a **reptile** as a pet because _____

_____ .

ENRICHMENT WORDS

Here are two more words to use when talking about animals.

1. **habitat** (hăb' ĭ tăt') *An animal's **habitat** is the place where it naturally lives and grows.* (noun)

When an animal is in danger of dying out, we should try to protect its **habitat.**

2. **omnivore** (ŏm' nə vôr') *An **omnivore** is a living thing that eats both plants and animals.* (noun)

A human being is an **omnivore.**

OFF THE PAGE

Think of an animal to research. Write one or two sentences to explain the answer to each of these questions:

1. Is it canine, feline, or reptilian?

2. Is it a vertebrate?

3. Is it a carnivore or a herbivore?

4. Is it domesticated?

carnivore? herbivore?

15 Review
Lessons 11–14

In this lesson, you will review the words and skills you have learned in the last four lessons. This will help you to remember them when you read and write.

A **MATCHING WORDS AND DEFINITIONS**
Write the word from the list that matches each definition.

> **particular   carnivore   spectacle   royal   primitive   vertebrate**

1. an animal with a backbone _____

2. careful about things _____

3. having to do with kings and queens _____

4. an animal that eats only meat _____

5. a large public show _____

6. in an early stage _____

B **USING WORDS IN CONTEXT** Use the words in each list to complete the paragraphs.

> **biologist   experiments   analyze   canine   feline**

   I really like science, so I plan to become a **(1)** _____.
I'd like to study **(2)** _____ and **(3)** _____
behavior because I think I can prove that cats and dogs are as smart as
people. I'll need to do some **(4)** _____ to prove my ideas.
Then I'll **(5)** _____ the results, write a book about what
I've discovered, and become famous!

> **emperor   debt   court   jester   spectacle**

   The **(6)** _____ was very unhappy, and the people of
his **(7)** _____ did everything they could to cheer him up.
They arranged a colorful **(8)** _____ of music and dance.
But nothing could bring a smile to their ruler's face. One day, an oddly

and colorfully dressed character arrived. "I am a **(9)** _____ ,"
he said, "and I will make your leader laugh." With that he pulled a rabbit
out of the emperor's crown, pulled coins from his nose, and recited a silly
poem in his ear. A broad, grateful smile spread over the emperor's face. "I
owe you a great **(10)** _____ ," he said. "You've made me feel
like a real person, not just a royal statue on a throne!"

C **CONTEXT AND DICTIONARY** You learned about
using context and a dictionary together in Lesson 11. Use the
context of the sentences below to figure out which meaning of the
word is used. Write the number of the definition on the line.

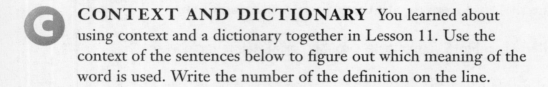

king *noun* **1.** A man who rules a nation. **2.** A person or thing that is
regarded as the most powerful or outstanding: *The lion is the king of the
jungle.* **3.** An important piece in the games of chess and checkers.
king (king) Δ *noun, plural* **kings**

1. We called Mark the **king** of dinosaurs because he knew so much about
   them. _____
2. Nika took my **king** and won the game of chess. _____
3. The **king** ruled his country fairly and wisely. _____

groom *noun* **1.** A person who takes care of horses. **2.** A bridegroom.
groom (gro͞om) Δ *noun, plural* **grooms**

4. The **groom** was late for his wedding because he couldn't find the ring.
   _____

5. When Melissa took riding lessons, the **groom** showed her how to put
   on the saddle and bridle. _____

D **TEST-TAKING STRATEGIES** In an **analogy,** both pairs of words are related in the same way.

Strategy: When you solve an analogy, think of how the first two words relate to each other. Then choose the word that makes the second pair relate the same way. Remember that you have learned three kinds of analogies:

- **synonyms** (<u>Swift</u> is to <u>fast</u> as <u>tardy</u> is to <u>late</u>.)
- **antonyms** (<u>Happy</u> is to <u>sad</u> as <u>full</u> is to <u>hungry</u>.)
- **type of** (<u>Checkers</u> is to <u>game</u> as <u>baseball</u> is to <u>sport</u>.)

Directions: Write the letter of the word that completes each analogy on the line.

1. <u>Saw</u> is to <u>tool</u> as <u>cow</u> is to _____.

    A. reptilian **B.** milk **C.** farm **D.** herbivore

2. <u>Ant</u> is to <u>insect</u> as <u>lion</u> is to _____.

    A. feline **B.** tiger **C.** canine **D.** bug

3. <u>Spaniel</u> is to <u>dog</u> as <u>dog</u> is to _____.

    A. canine **B.** royal **C.** carnivore **D.** beagle

4. <u>Domesticated</u> is to <u>wild</u> as <u>methodical</u> is to _____.

    A. careful **B.** sloppy **C.** primitive **D.** alert

5. <u>Plant-eater</u> is to <u>herbivore</u> as <u>meat-eater</u> is to _____.

    A. vertebrate **B.** canine **C.** reptilian **D.** carnivore

TEST-TAKING STRATEGIES On a **multiple-choice** test, you have to pick the correct answer out of several choices. Usually two or three answers seem like good choices, but only one answer is correct.

Strategy: Before you choose an answer, read both the question and answer choices at least two times. Does the answer you chose still make sense? If so, be sure to fill in the bubble completely and neatly.

Directions: Fill in the bubble next to the best answer to each question.

1. How would you describe a dog that is very aware of its surroundings?

   (**A**) relaxed   (**B**) alert   (**C**) particular   (**D**) royal

2. Which word is an example of a *feline?*

   (**A**) rat   (**B**) snake   (**C**) tiger   (**D**) canine

3. Which of the following has a strong odor?

   (**A**) potato   (**B**) onion   (**C**) paper   (**D**) apple

4. Which word describes someone who is very organized and careful?

   (**A**) primitive   (**B**) reptilian   (**C**) royal   (**D**) methodical

5. Who would you be most likely to find in a laboratory?

   (**A**) biologist   (**B**) opponent   (**C**) escort   (**D**) jester

ENRICHMENT WORDS

Draw a line between each Enrichment Word and its definition.

1. ambassador   place where an animal lives
2. mold   living thing that eats both plants and animals
3. habitat   rules of polite behavior
4. bacteria   a type of fungus
5. omnivore   one-celled organisms
6. etiquette   representative of a country

LESSON 16

FORMING NEW WORDS
Skill Lesson
roots and suffixes

walk-ing

In the next set of lessons, you will learn how to break apart words to find the meaning. You will also learn how to put word parts together to form new words. To do this, you must understand roots and suffixes.

A **ROOTS AND SUFFIXES** A **root** is the main meaning of the word. Some roots are words and some are not. A **suffix** comes after a root and often changes the number, the tense, or the part of speech of a word. In the word *sadly*, the root is *sad* and the suffix is *-ly*. When a suffix is written alone, it often has a line before it to show where the rest of the word hooks on. Each of the words below has a suffix. Decide what the suffix is and write it after the word. The first one is done for you.

1. kindness _____-ness_____
2. walking _____
3. triumphed _____
4. uselessly _____
5. enjoyment _____

Now that you have taken suffixes off, try putting them on. Add suffixes to the following roots as shown in the example. Notice that when a word ends in *y*, the *y* changes to *i* when a suffix is added.

Root	+	Suffix	=	Word
6. kind	+	-ness	=	_____kindness_____
7. dark	+	-ness	=	_____
8. happy	+	-ness	=	_____
9. agree	+	-ment	=	_____
10. entertain	+	-ment	=	_____

B **SUFFIXES -MENT AND -NESS** The suffixes you added in exercise A are *-ness* and *-ment*. Both suffixes make words into nouns. For example, the word *dark* is an adjective (describing word), but *darkness* is a noun, or a thing. To see how this works, use the words that you have created in sentences. The first sentence of each pair shows the root in boldface. To fill in the blank of the second sentence, add either *-ment* or *-ness* to the root.

1. Keisha is **kind** to animals. Because of her _____ , several neighbors ask her to take care of their pets when they are away.

2. Tamara is **happy** when she is helping people. She spreads _____ wherever she goes.

3. I **agree** with your plan. Let's put our _____ in writing.

4. Jerome can **entertain** himself with a good book. Jason's favorite form of _____ is a good computer game.

5. Timmy is afraid of **dark** rooms. He thinks that monsters are hiding in the _____ .

C **SUFFIXES -ABLE AND -IBLE** The suffix *-able*, sometimes spelled *-ible*, changes a verb to an adjective. It means "able to." For example:

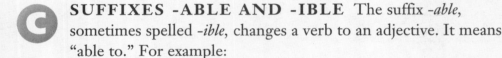

fix + able = fixable (able to be fixed)

Add the suffixes to the following words and write the definitions. When you add the suffix to a word ending with an *e*, you must drop the *e*.

1. like + able = ____likable (able to be liked)____

2. read + able = _____

3 laugh + able = _____

4. love + able = _____

Write the correct words on the lines.

5. **like/likable** Our new puppy is so _____ ! She is so cute and cuddly that she is easy to _____ .

6. **read/readable** I wanted to _____ the sports pages, but the newspaper was not _____ after it sat out in the rain.

7. **laugh/laughable** The band's music was so bad that it was

_____ . We tried not to _____ because

we didn't want to hurt the players' feelings.

8. **love/lovable** I _____ my dog Annie; she's the most

_____ dog I've ever known.

At times, this suffix can be attached to a root that is part of a word, rather than a whole word. When this happens, it is usually spelled *-ible*. In the examples below, separate the root from the *-ible*.

9. horrible _____horr-ible_____

10. possible _____

11. edible _____

12. flexible _____

D **SUFFIX -OUS** The suffix *-ous* changes a noun to an adjective. It means "full of."

poison + ous = poisonous (full of poison)

Add the suffix *-ous* to the following words and write the definitions. When you add *-ous* to a word that ends in *e*, you must drop the *e*.

1. danger + ous = _____

2. fame + ous = _____

3. joy + ous = _____

Write the correct words on the lines.

4. **danger/dangerous** We ran to the cellar when we heard about the

_____ tornado. We stayed there until the

_____ was past.

5. **fame/famous** Although _____ people may seem to

have everything, _____ alone does not bring happiness.

6. **joy/joyous** When he spotted his mother, Paolo's great

_____ showed in his smile. It was the most

_____ meeting I've ever seen.

Just like *-ible*, the suffix *-ous* can be attached to part of a word rather than a whole word. For example:

> **generous = gener + -ous** (willing to give)
>
> **serious = seri + -ous** (not joking or fooling)

Use these two words correctly in the sentences below.

7. If I become wealthy, I'm going to be very _____ to the poor.

8. Audrey is very _____ about becoming a doctor.

 SPELLING CHANGES Usually, suffixes are added to words without making any changes in the spelling of the words. However, sometimes the final *e* of a word must be dropped, or a final *y* must be changed to *i* when a suffix is added.

Look at these words and figure out what spelling changes have been made to the root. On the blanks, write the original spelling of each root word, plus the suffix.

Word	=	Root	+	Suffix
1. smokiness	=	smoky	+	-ness
2. teasable	=	_____	+	_____
3. continuous	=	_____	+	_____
4. tardiness	=	_____	+	_____
5. emptiness	=	_____	+	_____

LESSON 17

What a State!
suffixes -ment and -ness

settlement

A The suffixes *-ment* and *-ness* make words into nouns. Often they also mean a "state or quality of." You will meet thousands of words with these suffixes. The words in this lesson will help you to learn them.

1. **disappointment** (dĭs' ə **point'** mənt)
   Disappointment *is the feeling you get when you don't have what you hoped for.* (noun)
   To Cheri's **disappointment,** she was not chosen for the school play.

2. **embarrassment** (ĕm **băr'** əs mənt)
   Embarrassment *is a feeling of shame or self-consciousness.* (noun)
   Imagine my **embarrassment** when Mom showed my baby pictures to all my friends!

3. **improvement** (ĭm **prōōv'** mənt) *An* **improvement** *is a change that makes something better.* (noun)
   People who practice the piano often see great **improvement** in their playing.

4. **settlement** (sĕt' l mənt) *A* **settlement** *is a small community or a new colony.* (noun)
   In 1775, people from Monterey, California, formed a **settlement** that became San Francisco.

5. **illness** (ĭl' nĭs) *An* **illness** *is a sickness or disease.* (noun)
   Because of her **illness,** Tanya had to stay home from school.

6. **orderliness** (ôr' dər lĭ nəs)
   Orderliness *is a state of order that is arranged well; neatness.* (noun)
   Separating socks into groups by color shows **orderliness** in dresser drawers.

7. **seriousness** (sîr' ē əs nəs)
   Seriousness *means importance.* (noun)
   We realized the **seriousness** of the situation when we saw the rescue crew arrive.

8. **tenderness** (tĕn' dər nĭs) **Tenderness** *is a gentle feeling of love.* (noun)
   Langston Hughes felt great **tenderness** for the grandmother who raised him.

Draw a line between each vocabulary word and its definition.

1. seriousness   neatness

2. settlement   importance

3. orderliness   letdown feeling

4. disappointment   small community

© Great Source DO NOT COPY

Lesson 17 **65**

All the boldfaced words in the passage below include the suffixes *-ment* or *-ness*. Read the passage. Then answer the questions that follow.

A Cure for Smallpox

Have you ever heard of smallpox? For thousands of years it was an **illness** that killed many people. Smallpox was treated with great **seriousness** because it spread so easily. All the care and **tenderness** of parents could not protect their children from this disease. It covered the face, hands, and feet with sores. People who recovered had to deal with the **embarrassment** of ugly scars from these sores.

Today, the world is free of smallpox. How did this happen? Dr. Edward Jenner noticed that people who worked with cows did not get smallpox. Instead they got a mild disease called cowpox. Jenner thought that getting cowpox might keep people from getting smallpox. In 1796, Dr. Jenner put material from cowpox sores into a cut on the arm of eight-year-old James Phipps.

Several weeks later, he exposed the boy to smallpox, but James remained healthy. Because *vacca* means "cow" in Latin, Jenner called the process "vaccination."

Eventually, people throughout Europe and the American **settlements** were vaccinated against smallpox. But by 1967, two million people a year still died of smallpox. This large number of deaths was a **disappointment** to doctors. They wanted to change it. With **orderliness** and determination, the World Health Organization started a worldwide vaccination campaign. In just ten years, there was a great **improvement** in the situation. The last case of smallpox was reported in Somalia in 1977.

WORD LIST

disappointment

embarrassment

improvement

settlement

illness

orderliness

seriousness

tenderness

1. How was smallpox wiped out?

_____

_____

2. Use one of the following words to write a sentence about smallpox: *illness, seriousness, embarrassment.*

_____

_____

C Choose the word that best completes each sentence. Write it on the line.

1. The flu is a common _____ . *(settlement/illness)*

2. Our principal was pleased with the _____ we showed during the fire drill. *(embarrassment/orderliness)*

3. Raul couldn't hide his _____ when he lost the tennis match. *(tenderness/disappointment)*

4. Since I started spending more time on my homework, there has been a big _____ in my grades. *(improvement/orderliness)*

5. Paula blushed with _____ when she slipped and fell into the puddle. *(settlement/embarrassment)*

D Use each word and suffix to make a word taught in this lesson. Note that each word is either a verb or an adjective. When you add the suffixes, all words become nouns.

Root	+	Suffix	=	Word
1. serious	+	-ness	=	_____
2. embarrass	+	-ment	=	_____
3. tender	+	-ness	=	_____
4. settle	+	-ment	=	_____
5. improve	+	-ment	=	_____

OTHER FORMS

| disappointed |
| embarrassing |
| ill |
| improve |
| orderly |
| seriously |
| settle |
| tender |

E Complete each sentence with a phrase that makes sense. Note that some other forms of the vocabulary words have been used.

1. Something that should be taken **seriously** is _____
   _____ .

2. The best thing to do when you are **ill** is _____
   _____ .

3. When you **improve** something, _____
   _____ .

4. I was **disappointed** when _____
   _____ .

5. It would be **embarrassing** if _____
   _____ .

ENRICHMENT WORDS

Here are two more words that have a suffix. One has the suffix -*ness*. The other has the suffix -*ment*.

1. **achievement** (ə **chēv' mənt)** *Something that is done successfully is an* **achievement.** (noun)

   The students showed good **achievement** on their test scores.

2. **eagerness** (ē' gər nəs) **Eagerness** *is a strong desire to do something.* (noun)

   The dog showed her **eagerness** to play by bringing me her ball.

OFF THE PAGE

Choose one of these subjects to write about:

1. a time that caused you embarrassment

2. a time that caused you disappointment

Write a paragraph. Your first sentence should introduce what you are going to say. The next two to four sentences should tell what happened. The last sentence should wrap things up. You can also use other forms of the words, such as *embarrassing* or *disappointed*.

Ready and Able
suffixes -able and -ible

breakable

A The suffix *-able* changes a verb into an adjective. It means "capable of" or "able to be." The suffix *-ible* is like *-able*, but *-ible* is added to parts of a word rather than a whole word.

1. **breakable** (brāk' ə bəl) *Something* **breakable** *can be broken; it is capable of breaking.* (adjective)
When her two-year-old grandson came to visit, Mrs. Weiss put away her **breakable** vases.

2. **divisible** (dĭ vĭz' ə bəl) *Something* **divisible** *can be divided into parts; it is capable of being divided.* (adjective)
The number twenty-four is evenly **divisible** by two.

3. **feasible** (fē' zə bəl) *Something that is* **feasible** *is possible; it is capable of being done.* (adjective)
With heavy rain pouring down, our plans for a picnic were not **feasible.**

4. **legible** (lĕj' ə bəl) *Something that is* **legible** *is capable of being read.* (adjective)
Since I am left-handed, my writing is not **legible** if I use my right hand.

5. **noticeable** (nō' tĭ sə bəl) *Something that is* **noticeable** *can be easily seen; it is capable of being noticed.* (adjective)
There was a **noticeable** red stain on Perry's white shirt after he ate spaghetti.

6. **pliable** (plī' ə bəl) *Something that is* **pliable** *is easily bent or made into another shape; it is capable of being bent.* (adjective)
Dad pulled the **pliable** garden hose around the corner.

7. **suitable** (soo' tə bəl) *Something that is* **suitable** *is appropriate; it is right for a specific purpose.*
A bathing suit is not **suitable** clothing for a classroom.

8. **unreliable** (ŭn' rĭ lī' ə bəl) **Unreliable** *means not dependable; not to be trusted.* (adjective)
At camp, the hot water supply was **unreliable,** and we often had to take cold showers.

Draw a line from each word to its definition.

1. legible   capable of breaking

2. noticeable   appropriate

3. breakable   capable of being read

4. suitable   easily seen

5. unreliable   capable of being divided

6. divisible   not dependable

The boldfaced words in the passage below all contain the suffixes *-able* or *-ible*. Read the passage. Then answer the questions that follow.

Papyrus, Paper, and Parchment

Today paper is a common and cheap material, but this was not always so. The first writing was probably done using sticks on clay tablets. But these tablets were heavy and also **breakable.**

The Ancient Egyptians invented a material more **suitable** for writing. The stems of the papyrus plant were cut into thin pieces, pressed together into sheets, and dried. They formed **pliable** long sheets that could be rolled into scrolls. Papyrus scrolls were easily **divisible;** they could be cut to be as short as the writer wanted.

During the Middle Ages, papyrus was difficult to get in Europe, so it became more **feasible** to use parchment. This was made from animal hides that were worked on until they were thin and easy to write on.

Gradually, however, paper came into use. Invented in China in A.D. 105, paper was made by shredding and soaking the tough parts of plants and rags and straining them through a fine screen. Water drained through the screen, leaving a thin sheet, which dried into paper.

By 1700 paper was used all over the world. However, the supply of rags was **unreliable,** and people often ran out

of them. This made paper expensive. When people learned to make paper from wood, there was a **noticeable** increase in its use.

Long ago, most people could not read and write well enough to use papyrus, paper, or parchment. Some kings could not sign their names in **legible** ways. Instead, they made a single stroke with a feather pen. To prove they had written the letter, they pressed a personal stamp into hot wax to seal the letter.

WORD LIST

breakable

divisible

feasible

legible

noticeable

pliable

suitable

unreliable

1. What did people write on before paper became available? What were the drawbacks of these materials?

   _____

   _____

2. Is it more feasible for you to use paper, papyrus, or parchment? Why?

   _____

   _____

C Choose the word that best completes each sentence. Write it on the line.

1. We think it is _____ to turn the empty lot into a community garden. (*feasible/legible*)

2. Steve bent the _____ sheet of metal to form a roof for the birdhouse. (*unreliable/pliable*)

3. If you live in an earthquake zone, you shouldn't have a lot of _____ items. (*breakable/divisible*)

4. The local bus is _____, so we called a taxi to take us to the airport. (*suitable/unreliable*)

5. Marcia always writes our word webs on the board because her handwriting is so _____. (*legible/feasible*)

D Answer each riddle by writing the correct word from the word list.

1. I am easy to read. I am _____.

2. I can be divided. I am _____.

3. You can't miss me. I am _____.

4. You can bend me. I am _____.

5. I am easily damaged. I am _____.

OTHER FORMS

break

division

divide

legibly

notice

suited

reliable

rely

E Complete each sentence with a phrase that makes sense. Note that other forms of the vocabulary words have been used.

1. It is easy to **divide** _____

_____ .

2. To make a sign **noticeable,** you can _____

_____ .

3. Teachers want students to write **legibly** because _____

_____ .

4. I think I am **reliable** because _____

_____ .

5. When you handle something **breakable,** _____

_____ .

ENRICHMENT WORDS

Here are two more words that use the suffix -*able* or -*ible*.

1. **deplorable** (dĭ **plôr'** ə bəl) *Something* **deplorable** *is worthy of strong disapproval.* (adjective)

   My mother says that the condition of my room is **deplorable** and I must clean it.

2. **incredible** (ĭn **krĕd'** ə bəl) *Something* **incredible** *is very difficult to believe.* (adjective)

   Although it seemed **incredible,** Demetra raised her failing grade to an *A* in just one marking period.

OFF THE PAGE

Choose one of the other vocabulary words to explore in a word web. First write the word in the middle of a piece of paper. Then write as many other word forms as you can around the word. You can use a dictionary to help you. Finally take one word form and use it in a sentence.

divided   divide

dividing   divisible

divides   division

indivisible

numerous

LESSON 19 Full of It
suffix -ous

A The suffix *-ous* makes words into adjectives, or describing words. It often means means "full of." At times it is added to a whole word, and at times to a word part. All of the words below have this suffix.

1. **atrocious** (ə trō' shəs) *Something* **atrocious** *is very bad.* (adjective)
It is **atrocious** behavior to talk loudly during a movie or play.

2. **enormous** (ĭ nôr' məs) *Something that is* **enormous** *is very large.* (adjective)
The **enormous** pumpkin was four feet across and weighed 796 pounds.

3. **hazardous** (hăz' ər dəs) *Something* **hazardous** *is dangerous.* (adjective)
Smoking is **hazardous** to your health.

4. **monstrous** (mŏn' strəs) *Something* **monstrous** *is very large, very ugly, or very evil; it is like a monster.* (adjective)
A **monstrous** statue of an ugly creature stood at the gate of the ancient city to scare off robbers.

5. **numerous** (noo' mər əs) *Something* **numerous** *is made up of a large number; many.* (adjective)
Because of **numerous** errors in her paper, Amy had to copy it over.

6. **previous** (prē' vē əs) *Something* **previous** *took place earlier.* (adjective)
The post office forwarded my mail from my **previous** address to my new one.

7. **scrumptious** (skrŭmp' shəs) *Something that is* **scrumptious** *is very delicious.* (adjective)
Mrs. Torres ordered a **scrumptious** cake for Juan's tenth birthday party.

8. **vicious** (vĭsh' əs) *Something* **vicious** *is cruel and mean; dangerous.* (adjective)
The mother bear made a **vicious** attack on the men who tried to steal her cub.

Draw a line from each word to its definition.

1. numerous	delicious
2. hazardous	many
3. scrumptious	very bad
4. atrocious	dangerous
5. enormous	before
6. previous	mean
7. vicious	ugly
8. monstrous	very large

The boldfaced words in the passage below all have the suffix *-ous*. Read the passage. Then answer the questions that follow.

Australia's Amazing Flying Foxes

In 1770, an explorer in Australia told of a **monstrous-**looking animal with wings and horns. What could this have been? We now think it may have been the intelligent and affectionate bat known as the flying fox. Why would the explorer have found the bats strange? For one thing, these bats are **enormous**, with wingspreads of up to five feet. They were also quite **numerous.** In years **previous** to 1900, the bats' camps covered more than four miles each. When they flew, they blackened the sky. People found it an **atrocious** experience to be in a darkness filled with shrieking bats.

Flying foxes do not eat insects, as most bats do. Instead they eat fruits, flowers, and nectar. They find mangoes particularly **scrumptious.** As flying foxes travel from one fruit to another, they spread pollen that helps make more plants.

Unfortunately, as fruit trees in the wild forest have been destroyed, the bats have come to rely on fruit grown by human beings. This makes them **hazardous** to crops. Some farmers use nets to protect their fruit.

Bats have sometimes been thought of as **vicious** animals. But the flying fox has a gentle personality. Some people raise orphaned babies and then release them. These people find that the bats' fur is soft, and their wings feel like silk. Babies cling to caretakers and may even purr when petted. Flying foxes get to know their caretakers. After being released in the wild, one bat came back time after time to see his caregiver.

WORD LIST

atrocious

enormous

hazardous

monstrous

numerous

previous

scrumptious

vicious

1. Would you like to see some flying bats? Why?

_____

_____

2. Choose two of the following words. Use each word in a sentence that tells something about flying foxes: *vicious, monstrous, enormous, numerous*.

_____

_____

_____

C Choose the word that best completes each sentence. Write it on the line.

1. The man had such _____ table manners that he ate his peas with his fingers. (*numerous/atrocious*)

2. The old, rusty swing set is _____ because it could fall apart and hurt someone. (*enormous/hazardous*)

3. I can give you _____ reasons why I don't like that video game. (*numerous/monstrous*)

4. My new school has morning recess, but my _____ school had afternoon recess. (*vicious/previous*)

5. The crocodile opened its _____ mouth, showing rows of gleaming teeth. (*enormous/scrumptious*)

D Add *-ly* to each vocabulary word below to make it an adverb. An adverb describes how something is done or how someone behaves. For example, *fabulously* means "in a fabulous way."

Word	+	Suffix	=	Adverb
1. enormous	+	-ly	=	_____
2. monstrous	+	-ly	=	_____
3. scrumptious	+	-ly	=	_____
4. vicious	+	-ly	=	_____
5. atrocious	+	-ly	=	_____

OTHER FORMS

| atrociously |
| enormously |
| hazard |
| monster |
| monstrously |
| previously |
| scrumptiously |
| viciously |

E Complete each sentence with a phrase that makes sense. Note that some other forms of the vocabulary words have been used.

1. An example of a **hazard** is _____

_____ .

2. If you behave **atrociously,** _____

_____ .

3. A **scrumptious** dessert is _____

_____ .

4. There are **numerous** _____

_____ .

5. When you encounter a **vicious** animal, _____

_____ .

ENRICHMENT WORDS

Here are two more words that have the suffix *-ous*. Have you ever done anything *stupendous?*

1. **monotonous** (mə **nŏt'** n əs) *Something that is* **monotonous** *is very boring because it is always the same.* (adjective)

   The **monotonous** song repeated one short melody over and over.

2. **stupendous** (stoo **pĕn'** dəs) *Something that is* **stupendous** *is amazing or tremendous.* (adjective)

   After Kim's **stupendous** performance in gymnastics, the crowd stood and cheered.

OFF THE PAGE

Using the words *enormous* and *scrumptious,* write a paragraph about a delicious treat a baker made to impress the mayor of the city.

LESSON 20

Review
Lessons 16-19

In this lesson, you will review the words and skills you have learned in the last four lessons. This will help you to remember them when you read and write.

 A **MATCHING WORDS AND DEFINITIONS**
Write the word from the box that matches each definition.

orderliness   feasible   vicious   unreliable   tenderness

1. a gentle feeling of love _____
2. able to be done _____
3. not dependable; not to be counted on _____
4. neatness _____
5. violent, destructive, or mean _____

B **USING WORDS IN CONTEXT** Use the words in each list to complete the paragraphs.

embarrassment   improvement   suitable   numerous
atrocious   disappointment

The Museum of Bad Art displays only truly **(1)** _____ works. Good art is not **(2)** _____ for display here. Not surprisingly, **(3)** _____ pieces in the collection have not been signed by the artists. Some artists, though, don't feel any **(4)** _____ about having their work on display in this museum. To them, having no place to display their art is a **(5)** _____ . Having your work shown in the Museum of Bad Art is a big **(6)** _____ over not displaying it at all!

enormous   hazardous   suitable   seriousness

Tilly and Meg were in the middle of the field when the thunderstorm overtook them. They ran first for the shelter of the **(7)** _____ oak tree in the middle of the field. But Tilly remembered that tall trees are very **(8)** _____

Lesson 20 77

in thunderstorms because they are often struck by lightning. The girls decided that their parents' car, parked by the road, would make a more (9) _____ shelter. As they reached the car, Meg and Tilly heard a loud crash. The oak tree toppled to the ground, just where they had been standing. Then they realized the (10) _____ of their situation.

C **WRITING WORDS IN SENTENCES** Choose two of the words on each line to use in a sentence. You can change the form of the word if you like. (For example, *suitable* may be changed to *suitably* or *vicious* may be changed to *viciousness*.)

1. suitable   vicious   enormous

   _____

   _____

2. previous   disappointment   embarrassment

   _____

   _____

3. breakable   pliable   orderliness

   _____

   _____

4. divisible   scrumptious   improvement

   _____

   _____

5. seriousness   legible   illness

   _____

   _____

D **SUFFIXES** One way to read big words is to break them apart into roots and suffixes. Sometimes, when you take off a suffix, you have to change the spelling of the root to make a real word. On the lines, write the original spelling of each root and then the suffix. The first one is done for you.

Word	=	Root	+	Suffix
1. monstrous	=	monster	+	-ous
2. settlement	=	_____	+	_____
3. tenderness	=	_____	+	_____
4. divisible	=	_____	+	_____
5. hazard	=	_____	+	_____
6. improvement	=	_____	+	_____

E **TEST-TAKING STRATEGIES** In an **analogy,** both pairs of words are related in the same way.

Strategy: Sometimes, you will see an analogy on a test that has a blank somewhere besides at the end. Solve the analogy the same way as always.

Herbivore is to plant-eater as _____ is to meat-eater.

A herbivore is the same as a plant-eater, so think what is the same as a meat-eater. The answer is *carnivore.*

Here's one more example. Hint: To solve this analogy, think suffixes.

Monster is to monstrous as _____ is to numerous.

Monster plus the suffix *-ous* is *monstrous.* What word plus *-ous* is *numerous?* The answer is *number.*

Directions: Write the word that completes each analogy on the line.

1. Break is to breakable as _____ is to noticeable.

   A. broken   **B.** notice   **C.** note   **D.** pliable

2. Rich is to poor as _____ is to health.

   A. illness   **B.** doctor   **C.** apple   **D.** healthy

3. Later is to previous as _____ is to unreadable.

   A. legible   **B.** book   **C.** handwriting   **D.** before

4. <u>Monotonous</u> is to <u>boring</u> as _____ is to <u>dangerous</u>.

   A. song   **B.** sidewalk   **C.** rough   **D.** hazardous

5. <u>Tiny</u> is to <u>diminutive</u> as <u>huge</u> is to_____ .

   A. small   **B.** enormous   **C.** serious   **D.** scrumptious

F   **TEST-TAKING STRATEGIES** On a **multiple-choice** test, usually two or three answers seem like good choices. But only one answer is correct.

Strategy: Read through each question. Before you pick an answer, think of how you would answer the question. Look to see if your answer is one of the choices. If not, skip any answers you know are wrong and study the rest of the answers. Pick the best one.

Directions: Fill in the bubble next to the best answer to each question.

1. What is the feeling you have when you don't get something you want?

   (A) disappointment   (B) amusement   (C) enjoyment (D) tenderness

2. Which of the following describes something that can be done?

   (A) atrocious   (B) feasible   (C) divisible   (D) hazardous

3. How would you describe something that can be read?

   (A) legible   (B) pliable   (C) unreliable (D) suitable

4. How would you describe a slippery mountain road?

   (A) noticeable   (B) hazardous   (C) vicious   (D) previous

5. How would you describe someone who never shows up as planned?

   (A) numerous   (B) improvement (C) breakable   (D) unreliable

ENRICHMENT WORDS

Draw a line between each Enrichment Word and its definition.

1. incredible   worthy of strong disapproval
2. monotonous   amazing, tremendous
3. deplorable   very boring
4. eagerness   difficult to believe
5. stupendous   strong desire
6. achievement   something done well

GOING BEYOND WORDS

Skill Lesson
thesaurus, shades of meaning, idioms

Suppose you were writing about a cold day. Your writing will be boring if you always use the word *cold*. You might want to use different words to make your writing more interesting. Instead of cold, the day might be chilly or frosty. *Chilly* and *frosty* mean about the same as, or are **synonyms** for, *cold*. You can find lots of synonyms in a book called a **thesaurus.**

A **USING THE THESAURUS** Let's look at an example of a paragraph that could use some synonyms.

chilly

> We had a good day on the lake yesterday. The weather was good, and the fishing was very good. At first, though, we didn't catch anything. Then Mr. Chen rowed by and gave us some good information. He told us where the fish were biting. He's a good fisherman, so we decided to take his advice. After we moved to the new spot, we caught a lot of fish. All in all, it was a good day.

cold

frosty

Circle the word *good* each time it is used in the paragraph. The writer has used the word good _____ times.

To find synonyms for good, you could look in a **thesaurus.** A thesaurus lists words in alphabetical order, just like a dictionary. Instead of definitions, a thesaurus has a list of synonyms. Look at this thesaurus entry for *good* to find other words that could be used instead:

good *adjective* 1. enjoyable, fine, nice, excellent, great 2. beneficial, favorable, helpful, useful. 3. able, capable, competent, skilled, skillful. 4. dependable, reliable, sound. 5. nice, well-behaved, honorable.

The numbers in the thesaurus tell us that the words form different groups of meaning. For example, group 2 has words that mean "good," but also have a "helpful" meaning. Group 5 words mean "good," in a well-behaved way.

How do you choose? Synonyms often have different **shades of meaning,** or small differences in meaning. Two synonyms may differ in "how much." For example, *excellent* seems a lot better than *nice*. Synonyms may also describe different things. You certainly wouldn't choose *well-behaved* to describe a good day. When you choose synonyms, then, you will need to use your own experience and common sense. Sometimes, if you're not sure about the shades of meaning, you will need to check the definitions in a dictionary.

Now let's improve the paragraph about fishing. Choose the word that has the correct shade of meaning and write it on the line. Use a dictionary to help you sort out the different shades of meaning.

   We had an **(1)** _____ (*enjoyable/able*) day on the lake yesterday. The weather was **(2)** _____ (*well-behaved/fine*), and the fishing was **(3)** _____ (*capable/excellent*). At first, though, we didn't catch anything. Then Mr. Chen rowed by and gave us some **(4)** _____ (*honorable/useful*) information. He told us where the fish were biting. He's a **(5)** _____ (*skilled/nice*) fisherman, so we decided to take his advice. After we moved to the new spot, we caught a lot of fish. All in all, it was a **(6)** _____ (*dependable/great*) day.

B **SHADES OF MEANING** Here are some more examples of words that have different shades of meaning. Read each pair of words and think which word fits the context best. Then write the word that best completes each sentence. Use a dictionary if you need more information to understand the differences between the words.

large   huge

1. The _____ size of the tidal wave was very frightening.

2. Rosa's mother told her to be sure to buy _____ eggs, not medium.

grab   take

3. Leo tried to _____ the balloon before it floated away.

4. Please don't _____ more than one cupcake.

hop   leap

5. We enjoy watching the baby bunnies _____ around in the garden.

6. It was said that the superhero could _____ tall buildings with a single bound.

C **USING THE RIGHT WORD** Use the dictionary entries to help you place the synonyms in the sentences.

> **idea** (ī dē' ə) A thought or plan carefully formed in the mind. *noun*
> **hunch** (hŭnch) A feeling or belief without any reason for it. *noun*

1. Stefan worked for a long time on the _____ for his new invention.

2. I followed a _____ and discovered the treasure buried under the elm tree.

> **group** (grōōp) A number of people or things gathered together. *noun*
> **mob** (mŏb) A large crowd that behaves badly. *noun*

3. The angry _____ burst through the barriers.

4. I'm going to join an after-school poetry _____ .

> **moist** (moist) Slightly wet. *adjective*
> **soggy** (sô' gē) Soaked with water. *adjective*

5. We sank up to our knees in the _____ muck.

6. When I have a fever, my mother puts a _____ , cool washcloth on my forehead.

> **look** (lŏŏk) To use the eyes to see. *verb*
> **inspect** (ĭn spĕkt') To examine in a careful, organized way. *verb*

7. I taught my little brother to _____ both ways when he crosses the street.

8. At least once a week, I carefully _____ my dog's fur for fleas.

> **break** (brāk) To crack or split. *verb*
> **smash** (smăsh) To break into pieces. *verb*

9. If you _____ that cookie in half, we can share it.

10. Sarita wanted to see the inside of the rock, so she used a hammer to _____ it.

IDIOMS When you think about shades of meaning, you think about what two words have in common. You also think about the little differences in meaning. This is "going beyond words." Another time when you have to go beyond the exact words is when you read **idioms.**

Idioms are phrases, or groups of words, that have a special meaning. This meaning is different from what the phrase seems to mean on the surface.

For example, what do you picture when someone says, "Oh, you're just pulling my leg!" Do you picture someone tugging on a person's leg? If you consider what this phrase seems to mean, then that's just what you will picture! But because this is an idiom, it has the special meaning of "teasing" or "fooling."

Here are several common idioms. They are underlined in each sentence. Use the sentence context to figure out their meanings. Circle the correct meaning for each idiom.

1. When Rebecca came home from school, she went to her room to <u>hit the books</u>. *(throw books on the floor/study)*

2. "This TV show is <u>for the birds</u>," said Yoshi as he clicked off the television. *(terrible/all about birds)*

3. Ms. Giorgio's garden is always beautiful. I think she <u>has a green thumb</u>. *(wears green gloves/is a good gardener)*

4. Please <u>drop me a line</u> during vacation so I will know how you're doing. *(go fishing/write a note)*

5. "You're not the only one who thinks we have too much homework," said Joe. "We are all <u>in the same boat</u>." *(in the same situation/in a canoe)*

LESSON 22

Not as They Seem
idioms

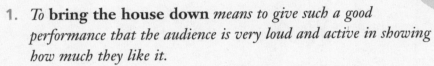

A An idiom is a group of words that has a special meaning separate from the meanings of the individual words. One of the idioms below is "eat your words." It does not mean to actually eat words! The whole idiom has its own meaning.

1. *To* **bring the house down** *means to give such a good performance that the audience is very loud and active in showing how much they like it.*

   Ice skater Michelle Kwan **brings the house down** after her fabulous performances.

2. *A* **cliff-hanger** *is a break in a story at a point of great suspense, where we wonder what is about to happen.*

   Cliff-hangers often occur just before television commercials.

3. *To* **eat your words** *is to take back what you said or admit you were wrong.*

   "I'm going to make you **eat your words**," said Matt to his brother, who said Matt couldn't ride a skateboard.

4. *To* **hit the road** *means to start on a journey, particularly by car.*

   We planned to leave early, but it was noon before we **hit the road.**

5. *To* **lend a hand** *is to help someone out.*

   Could you **lend a hand** by carrying those boxes upstairs?

6. *To* **look down your nose** *is to think that other people are not as good as you.*

   People in the play **looked down their noses** at others who didn't get parts.

7. *To* **be on thin ice** *is to be in risk of danger or trouble.*

   "You'll **be on thin ice** if you forget your homework one more time," warned the teacher.

8. *To* **put your foot in your mouth** *is to say something embarrassing or hurtful to others.*

   I **put my foot in my mouth** by talking about the party, when my friend hadn't been invited.

B The idioms are boldfaced in the passage below. Read the passage. Then answer the questions that follow.

Idioms That Make Our Language More Colorful

Idioms add variety and interest to our language. For example, after a wonderful concert finishes, we may clap, shout, and even stomp on the floor. We make so much noise that it seems like we will **bring the house down.**

Years ago, movies appeared as serials. That is, a part of the story was shown every week. To tempt people to see the next part, each one ended in an exciting way. Perhaps a person was hanging on the edge of a cliff, about to fall or be rescued. We call story pauses like these **cliff-hangers.**

Have you ever said something that you later realized was very wrong? To get rid of what you said forever, you might have wanted to **eat your words.**

When we start on a trip, our feet **hit the road.** For this reason, to *hit the road* means to begin a trip.

Lend a hand probably comes from helping by carrying things. However, we *lend a hand* by helping someone out in any way.

Kings and queens often sat so high on their thrones that they looked down at other people. Perhaps they thought they were better than others, so to **look down your nose** means to feel others are not as good as you.

Skating **on thin ice** is dangerous because the ice can easily crack. We use this image as an idiom in everyday life. If you have been warned not to be late again, you are **on thin ice.** The next time you come in late, you will probably be in trouble.

When you **put your foot in your mouth** you say something embarrassing or bad. It is said that, long ago, the Emperor of China actually forced people to put their feet in their mouths when they did something very wrong.

WORD LIST

bring the house down

cliff-hanger

eat your words

hit the road

lend a hand

look down your nose

be on thin ice

put your foot in your
  mouth

1. How can **putting your foot in your mouth** put you **on thin ice** with someone? Can **eating your words** solve the problem? Explain.

_____

_____

_____

_____

2. Choose one idiom and tell how you would use it.

_____

_____

C Choose the idiom that best fits each example. Write it on the line.

1. "What an ugly jacket!" you say to Ari, pointing to a jacket left on the bleachers. "That's my jacket," replies Ari. You have just _____. *(brought the house down/ put your foot in your mouth)*

2. The hero of the TV mini-series is tied up in a dungeon; the words "To be continued" flash on the screen. It's a _____. *(cliff-hanger/bringing the house down)*

D Write the idiom that can correctly replace the underlined words in each sentence.

1. I was already <u>in danger of being in trouble</u> with my brother, and then I broke his fishing rod. _____

2. The response to the band's performance is sure to <u>be wild clapping and cheering</u>. _____

3. You shouldn't <u>think you are better than</u> someone else just because they don't wear expensive clothes. _____

4. We're going to <u>start on our journey</u> bright and early tomorrow morning. _____

5. It gives me a good feeling to <u>help out</u> at the homeless shelter on weekends. _____

E   Complete each sentence with a phrase that makes sense.

1. Don't **look down your nose** at other people because _____

    _____ .

2. If you are **on thin ice,** you had better   _____

    _____ .

3. Before you **hit the road,** be sure to   _____

    _____ .

4. If a performer **brings the house down,** she or he should   _____

    _____ .

5. When you **lend a hand,** you feel   _____

    _____ .

ENRICHMENT WORDS

Here are two more idioms. Have you heard them before?

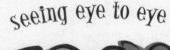

1. **see eye to eye** *People who* **see eye to eye** *agree with each other.*

    My parents and my teacher **see eye to eye** about my need to study more.

2. **take with a grain of salt** *When we take something* **with a grain of salt,** *we do not take it seriously.*

    I took my brother's complaint **with a grain of salt,** because he thinks everything is bad.

OFF THE PAGE

Select one of the idioms to illustrate. Think about the picture you get in your mind when you hear the idiom. Label your picture with the idiom and a brief definition.

Borrowed Words
words from other languages

A Many words in English came from other languages. The words below are all from languages other than English, such as French or Spanish.

AUSTRALIA

boomerang

1. **aficionado** (ə fĭsh' ē ə nä' dō) *An* **aficionado** *is a fan or admirer who knows a great deal about something.* (noun)
Ravi is a movie **aficionado** who sees movies three days a week.

2. **bonanza** (bə năn' zə) *A* **bonanza** *is something that is valuable or makes lots of money; a source of riches.* (noun)
The collection of rare stamps in the basement proved to be a **bonanza.**

3. **boomerang** (boo' mə răng') *When something* **boomerangs,** *it comes back to the person who started it.* (verb)
The baseball star's rudeness **boomeranged,** and soon fans began to dislike him.

4. **bouquet** (bō kā') *A* **bouquet** *is a bunch of flowers, often tied together.* (noun)
Mrs. Keenan brought a **bouquet** of roses to her dinner hosts.

5. **cuisine** (kwĭ zēn') *A* **cuisine** *is a style of cooking.* (noun)
French **cuisine** is famous throughout the world.

6. **lilac** (lī' lǝc)
Lilac *is a pale purple color. The lilac flower often has this color.* (adjective)
My mother's favorite dress is **lilac** and pink.

7. **tote** (tōt) *To* **tote** *something is to carry it.* (verb)
We had to **tote** the heavy bags of books up three flights of stairs.

8. **tycoon** (tī koon') *A* **tycoon** *is a person who is very successful in business.* (noun)
Madame C. J. Walker was one of the first African American women to become a **tycoon.**

Draw a line between each vocabulary word and its definition.

1. cuisine   come back
2. tycoon   source of riches
3. boomerang   successful business person
4. bonanza   cooking style
5. lilac   bunch of flowers
6. tote   purple color
7. bouquet   admirer
8. aficionado   carry

All the boldfaced words in the passage below come from other languages. Read the passage. Then answer the questions that follow.

Words Borrowed from Other Languages

English has borrowed many words from other languages. The French are known for their fine food. It is not surprising, then, that the word **cuisine,** meaning "a certain type of cooking," is from French. A vase of flowers on the table helps us to enjoy our food. The word **bouquet** is also taken from French. It comes from the word for *forest.*

We have borrowed many words from Spanish, also. Hundreds of years ago, Spanish explorers searched the Americas for gold. When they found rich deposits, they called them **bonanzas.** The Spanish word **aficionado,** taken from the word for *love* or *affection,* is used to describe someone who loves a sport, art, or pastime very much.

Native tribes of Australia have a curved stick called a boomerang that they used for hunting. It can be thrown in such a way that it will come back to the person who threw it. So, to **boomerang** means "to come back."

In the 1800s, the Japanese took a word from the Chinese to describe a prince of great power. Today, **tycoon** means "a business person of great wealth and achievement."

Lilac has a rich and interesting history. It came into English through Arabic, but before this, it was a Persian word. Originally, it was spoken in Sanskrit, an ancient language of India, and meant "dark blue."

The word **tote** probably came from Africa through the Bantu tribe. Similar words in Kongo and Swahili mean "to pick up."

bouquet

WORD LIST

aficionado

bonanza

boomerang

bouquet

cuisine

lilac

tote

tycoon

1. Think of an aficionado that you know. What does that person enjoy?

_____

_____

2. Choose one of the following word pairs and write one sentence using both words: **aficionado/cuisine, tycoon/bonanza,** or **lilac/bouquet.**

_____

_____

C Choose the word that best completes each sentence. Write the word on the line.

1. Puerto Rican _____ features delicious dishes such as pastales and sweet rice. *(boomerang/cuisine)*

2. During the California Gold Rush, people looked for gold in the hills, hoping to find a _____ . *(bouquet/bonanza)*

3. We had to _____ all of our camping gear four miles into the woods. *(tote/boomerang)*

4. Marc is an _____ of classical music. *(tycoon/aficionado)*

5. The wealthy _____ bought an entire city block so he could build a skyscraper. *(tycoon/lilac)*

D Use the words in the word list to answer these questions. Write the words on the line.

1. List two words from the list that are people.

_____

2. List two words that are things you can hold in your hand.

_____

3. List one word that has to do with food.

_____

Complete each sentence with a phrase that makes sense.

1. My favorite **cuisine** is _____
   _____ .

2. A good reason to give someone a **bouquet** is _____
   _____ .

3. You might **tote** a heavy suitcase because _____
   _____ .

4. A **tycoon** has _____
   _____ .

5. When I threw the **boomerang,** _____
   _____ .

ENRICHMENT WORDS

Here are two more words that come from another language. This time, the language is French.

1. **cliché** (klē shā') *A* **cliché** *is an overused, tired expression.* Cliché *is from French.* (noun)

   One popular **cliché** is "red as a rose."

2. **curfew** (kûr' fyoo) *A* **curfew** *is the time that a person must be off the street, or at home.* Curfew *comes from the French words for "cover the fire," which you would do before going to bed at night.* (noun)

   I made it home just before my eight o'clock **curfew.**

OFF THE PAGE

Many countries and cultures have excellent cuisines. Name one type of cuisine you enjoy. Name and describe two of your favorite dishes and explain why they are your favorites.

cuisine

LESSON 24

Name Game
words that come from names

A Did you know that some words we use nearly every day are borrowed from people's names? The words below all come from names.

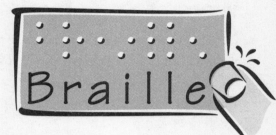

1. **boycott** (boi' kŏt') *To* **boycott** *is to protest by refusing to do business with or buy from a store, company, person, or nation.* (verb)
   Neighborhood people decided to **boycott** the pet store that sold sick animals.

2. **Braille** (brāl) **Braille** *is an alphabet for blind people made from raised dots.* (noun)
   My neighbor, who is blind, reads several books a month in **Braille.**

3. **Fahrenheit** (făr' ən hīt') **Fahrenheit** *is the name of a temperature scale.* (adjective)
   Water freezes at 32 degrees **Fahrenheit** and boils at 212 degrees.

4. **jumbo** (jŭm' bō) **Jumbo** *means very large.* (adjective)
   We enjoy watching videos on the **jumbo** television screen.

5. **maverick** (măv' ər ĭk) *A* **maverick** *is an independent-minded person; a rebel.* (noun)
   The senator is a **maverick** politician who follows his own beliefs.

6. **pasteurization** (păs' chər ĭ zā' shən) **Pasteurization** *is a process of killing bacteria by heating a liquid.* (noun)
   Pasteurization has made milk safer to drink than it was 150 years ago.

7. **saxophone** (săk' sə fōn') *A* **saxophone** *is a wind instrument played by mouth that has finger controls and a cone-like tube.* (noun)
   The **saxophone** is an important instrument in jazz.

8. **watt** (wŏt) *A* **watt** *is a unit of electrical or mechanical power.* (noun)
   The brightness of a light bulb is measured in **watts.**

Draw a line between each vocabulary word and its definition.

1.	maverick	process that kills bacteria
2.	pasteurization	alphabet of raised dots
3.	Braille	to protest by not buying
4.	boycott	rebel
5.	watt	musical instrument
6.	Fahrenheit	unit of electrical power
7.	saxophone	temperature scale
8.	jumbo	very large

© Great Source DO NOT COPY

Lesson 24 93

All the boldfaced words in the passage below come from names.
Read the passage. Then answer the questions that follow.

Words That Come from Names

Many words in English come from names. Louis Braille was only 3 years old when he was blinded by an accident. Because he wanted to read, he started working on an alphabet for the blind in 1924, when he was 15 years old. The system of raised dots he invented is now called **Braille.**

a 60-watt lightbulb

In the 1860s, another Frenchman, Louis Pasteur, discovered that heating milk killed the harmful bacteria that often made people sick. Today, this widely used method is known as **pasteurization.** Almost all of our milk is now pasteurized.

In Poland, Gabriel Fahrenheit invented the first easily used thermometer. It measured the temperature of the air and also body heat. The settings he chose for the thermometer are now known as the **Fahrenheit** scale.

Irish people in the 1800s objected to the high rents charged by Captain James Boycott. They refused to work on his lands or to deal with him. This type of treatment is now known as to **boycott.**

The unit that measures electrical or mechanical power—the **watt**— was named in honor of the Scottish man who invented the steam engine, James Watt. The power of the steam engine was measured in watts. Today you probably know the word from light bulbs, whose brightness is also measured in watts.

Samuel A. Maverick was a Texan who, in the late 1800s, refused to brand his calves. Whenever people found an unbranded calf, they would say, "It's a **Maverick.**" Soon, the word came to mean someone who doesn't go along with a group.

Working in Belgium, Antoine Sax invented and improved many musical instruments. One of these instruments is now known as the **saxophone.**

Words have also come to us from animal names. **Jumbo** was a huge African elephant who performed in P. T. Barnum's circus. *Jumbo* may have come from the word for "chief" in Swahili. In English, however, it now means very large.

WORD LIST

boycott

Braille

Fahrenheit

jumbo

maverick

pasteurization

saxophone

watt

1. List three words that are named after inventors.

_____

2. Choose two words from this lesson and write one sentence that uses them both. You can change the form of the words. For example, you can use *boycotted*.

_____

C Choose the word that completes each sentence. Write the word on the line.

1. We might _____ a store that sold things made by children too young to work. *(boycott/jumbo)*

2. In the United States we use the _____ scale to measure temperature, but many other countries use the Celsius scale. *(Fahrenheit/saxophone)*

3. You should use at least a sixty-_____ light bulb for your reading lamp. *(jumbo/watt)*

4. Our library is trying to raise money to order more books in _____ . *(pasteurization/Braille)*

5. Liz really likes popcorn, so she always buys the _____ size bucket. *(maverick/jumbo)*

D Complete the crossword puzzle with words from the word list.

Across

3. musical instrument
4. system of printing for blind readers
5. to protest by not buying

Down

1. very large
2. rebel

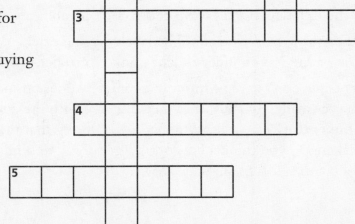

E Complete each sentence with a phrase that makes sense. Note that another form of one vocabulary word has been used.

1. A **maverick** will never _____

_____ .

2. The group decided to **boycott** the store because _____

_____ .

3. To read in **Braille,** you _____

_____ .

4. Milk that is not **pasteurized** is _____

_____ .

5. To play a **saxophone,** _____

_____ .

saxophone

ENRICHMENT WORDS

Here are two more words that come from names.

1. **dunce** (dŭns) **Dunce** *comes from the name of a Scotsman whose beliefs were thought to be stupid. It means "a stupid person."* (noun)
   I felt like a **dunce** when I got the easy math problem wrong.

2. **vandalism** (văn' dl ĭz' əm) **Vandalism** *comes from the name of a tribe that destroyed ancient Rome. It means "the destruction or damaging of property."* (noun)
   Because of **vandalism,** there was no equipment left on the playground.

OFF THE PAGE

Choose one of the following topics to write a paragraph about.

1. Think of a famous person who could be labeled a **maverick.** Write about why he or she was an independent thinker or rebel.

2. Sometimes people don't agree with how a company does business or how a product is made. To show that they disagree with the company, the people **boycott** it. That is, they don't buy anything that the company makes. Do you think a boycott is a good way to send a message to a company? Explain your answer.

LESSON 25

Review
Lessons 21-24

In this lesson, you will review the words and skills you have learned in the last four lessons. This will help you to remember them when you read and write.

A **MATCHING WORDS AND DEFINITIONS**
Write the word from the list that matches each definition.

> **cliff-hanger   pasteurization   cuisine   jumbo   watt**

1. point of great suspense in a story _____

2. a style of cooking _____

3. very large _____

4. process of killing bacteria in liquid _____

5. a measure of electrical power _____

B **USING WORDS IN CONTEXT** Use the words in each box to complete the paragraphs.

> **tote   cuisine   lend a hand   bouquet   aficionado
> bring the house down**

Last year, my father visited Thailand and had a chance to sample Thai

(1) _____ in some fine restaurants. He quickly became an

(2) _____ of Thai food. After taking a cooking class, he

began to **(3)** _____ home bags and bags of special Thai

ingredients. His plan was to cook a big Thai meal for Sunday dinner. My

mother offered to **(4)** _____, but he wanted to do it all

himself. He did allow me to put together a **(5)** _____ of

flowers for the table, though. At the end of the meal, we cheered loudly.

"Wow," said Dad, "I didn't think a simple meal would be good enough to

(6) _____!"

| tycoon | maverick | hit the road | bonanza |

The old miner had **(7)** _____ for California the moment he heard talk of gold in the hills. For many years now, he had wandered through the hills, dressed in rags, while he searched for his **(8)** _____ . He had only his mule to keep him company, but he didn't feel lonely. He'd always been a **(9)** _____ , going his own way instead of following the crowd. He knew that one day he'd find his gold. Then he would become a **(10)** _____ , dress in expensive suits, and travel in style.

C **REVIEWING IDIOMS** Read each of the following paragraphs. Then choose the idiom from the box that best fits the situation.

| eat your words | lend a hand | look down their noses at |
| put your foot in your mouth | | |

Rachel goes to a very old, private school. The other students are all from wealthy families. Their parents give them large allowances. Rachel's parents are poor. She gets a very small allowance. The other students think that Rachel is not as good as they are because she doesn't have much money.

1. _____ .

You come through the front door and call out to your mother, "Mom, did you see that ugly car out front? Anyone who would buy such an ugly car ought to be arrested!" You walk into the kitchen and see your uncle sitting at the table. "That's my brand new car," he says.

2. _____ .

"You'll never even finish this race," you tell your sister. "You haven't trained at all. These other runners have been training for months. You'll collapse, and we'll have to take you home on a stretcher!" The next day, your sister wins the race in record time.

3. _____ .

TEST-TAKING STRATEGIES An **analogy** is a way of connecting words. If you know how one pair of words is related, then you can understand how another pair of words fits together.

Strategy: The analogies you have seen in this book so far all have the missing word at the end. Sometimes, the blank is in another place in the analogy. No matter where the missing word is, you solve the analogy the same way. This analogy is about things that are used to do something.

> **shovel : digging : : _____ : raking**
> (**A**) spoon   (**B**) scissors   (**C**) mowing   (**D**) rake

A shovel is used for digging, so which word choice is used for raking? Both a spoon and scissors can be used for something, but not raking. *Mowing* is not a tool. A rake is used for raking. You can check your answer by saying the analogy as a sentence:

> A shovel is used for digging, and a rake is used for raking.

Directions: Fill in the bubble next to the word that best completes each analogy.

1. **jog : run : : _____ : carry**
   (**A**) tote   (**B**) lose   (**C**) drop   (**D**) arms

2. **admirer : aficionado : : _____ : maverick**
   (**A**) rebel   (**B**) fan   (**C**) watt   (**D**) cowboy

3. **pen : writing : : _____ : music**
   (**A**) singing   (**B**) Braille   (**C**) saxophone (**D**) pencil

4. **maple : tree : : _____ : color**
   (**A**) oak   (**B**) lilac   (**C**) crayon   (**D**) paint

5. **huge: jumbo : : _____ : boycott**
   (**A**) small   (**B**) large   (**C**) company   (**D**) protest

E **TEST-TAKING STRATEGIES** On a **multiple-choice** test, you have to pick the correct answer out of several choices.

Strategy: Read through each question. Before you pick an answer, think of how you would answer the question. Look to see if your answer is one of the choices. Check your answer by reading the whole question again with your answer. Then carefully and completely fill in the bubble.

Directions: Fill in the bubble next to the best answer to each question.

1. What form of protest might a group use to put pressure on a large company that is dumping chemicals into the river?

   (A) Use Braille to write a book about chemicals (B) play a song on the saxophone (C) boycott the company (D) lend a hand

2. What happens when something *boomerangs?*

   (A) it explodes (B) it melts (C) it is on thin ice
   (D) it comes back to the person who started it

3. Which of the following is most likely to make you rich?

   (A) bonanza (B) cuisine (C) bouquet (D) lilac

4. If a singer brings the house down, what does it say about his performance?

   (A) people hated it (B) people loved it (C) no one cared
   (D) people left early

5. Which of the following would be most likely to be very wealthy?

   (A) aficionado (B) tycoon (C) maverick (D) Fahrenheit

ENRICHMENT WORDS

Draw a line between each Enrichment Word and its definition.

1. cliché — destruction of property
2. dunce — agree
3. vandalism — a stupid person
4. take with a grain of salt — overused expression
5. curfew — not take seriously
6. see eye to eye — time to be home

LOOKING INTO WORDS

Skill Lesson
prefixes and roots

A **INTRODUCING PREFIXES** A **prefix** is a word part added to the beginning of a root. When a prefix is added, it changes the meaning of the root. Learning the meanings of prefixes helps you figure out meanings of many words.

A **root** is the most important part of a word. Some roots are words that can stand on their own. Others are not whole words until a prefix is added.

The words below both have the prefix *pre-*. *Pre-* means "before." (The line after a prefix shows you where the root attaches.) Draw a line between the prefix and the rest of the word.

1. preflight

2. predict

Now look the part of the word after your line. That is the root. Underline it.

3. Which root is a word? _____

4. Which root is not a word? _____

Use the meaning of the prefix and the meaning of the root, in this case a word, to write a meaning for *preflight*.

5. *Preflight* means _____ .

Predict is a little harder to figure out. The root *dict* comes from Latin and means "to say." Now write what you think *predict* means.

6. *Predict* means _____ .

The following words each have a prefix. Take each word apart, as shown in the example. Put a star by the roots that are words.

7. prefer = _____pre-_____ + _____fer_____

8. prepay = _____ + _____

9. precook = _____ + _____

10. preheat = _____ + _____

B **PREFIXES** *pre-* **AND** *post-* You can use prefixes to help you understand what words mean. Remember that the prefix *pre-* means "before." The prefix *post-* means "after." Fill in the blanks to help you understand what each boldfaced word means.

1. A **pretest** is a test _____ you learn something.

2. A **posttest** is a test _____ you learn something.

3. The **predawn** means the time _____ dawn.

4. **Preschool** classes are classes that you attend _____ you go to school.

5. A **postwar** treaty is a treaty made _____ the war.

6. When we **prearrange** something, we arrange it _____.

7. **Postoperative** care means the care _____ an operation.

8. To **prepare** something is to get it ready _____ you need it.

C **PREFIX** *co-* The prefix *co-* means "together" or "with." It may be spelled as *col-*, *com-*, *con-*, or *cor-* when it is attached to different roots. These spelling changes help us pronounce the words more easily. Fill in the blanks to explain these *co-* words.

1. A **coworker** works _____ you.

2. When you **cooperate** with others, you operate _____ others.

3. When two things **connect,** they come _____.

4. A **coauthor** is an author who writes _____ another author.

5. To **confide** in a friend is to share secrets _____ your friend.

6. Something that **concerns** your family has to do _____ your family.

7. When you **combine** forces, you bring your forces _____.

8. Bees that stay in a **compact** cluster stay closely _____.

D **PREFIXES** *anti-* **AND** *mis-* The prefix *anti-* means "against" or "opposite." The prefix *mis-* means "bad, badly, wrong, or wrongly." Fill in the blanks to explain the *anti-* and *mis-* words.

1. **Antiwar** means _____ war.

2. **Antilitter** means _____ litter.

3. **Antislavery** means _____ slavery.

4. An **antitoxin** is a substance that works _____ a toxin.

5. To **mistreat** means to treat someone _____.

6. To **misspell** means to spell _____.

7. **Misfortune** is _____ fortune.

8. **Misconduct** is _____ conduct.

E **PRACTICING PREFIXES** Use the prefix meanings from this lesson to figure out words from the following lessons. Circle the correct choice for each sentence.

1. **Antisocial** means (*against/with*) society.

2. A **comrade** is someone who goes (*before/with*) you.

3. A **premature** event occurs (*before/after*) it is supposed to occur.

4. A **mismatch** is a match that is (*bad/good*).

5. **Mistrust** is (*before/bad*) trust.

6. To **coexist** is to exist (*with/against*) others.

7. When you **predict** something, you tell about it (*before/after*) it happens.

8. The **preteen** years are the years (*before/after*) the teens.

mismatch

F **SORTING WORDS** Sort the words by prefix.
Write each word in the correct box.

antiwar	postwar	posttest
mislabel	prepare	pretest
connect	misspell	mistreat
prepay	confide	postseason
coworker	antilitter	antitoxin

Pre-
_____
_____
_____

Post-
_____
_____
_____

Co-
_____
_____
_____

Anti-
_____
_____
_____

Mis-
_____
_____
_____

Before and After
prefixes pre- and post-

a preteen

A The prefix *pre-* means "before," and the prefix *post-* means "after." The words below all include these prefixes.

1. **posterity** (pŏ stěr' ĭ tē) **Posterity** *refers to people who are not born yet; they come* **after** *others.* (noun)
Wolfgang Mozart left beautiful music to **posterity.**

2. **postpone** (pōst' pōn') *When we* **postpone** *something, we delay it or do it* **after** *we had planned to.* (verb)
Because of rain, we had to **postpone** the picnic until next week.

3. **postseason** (pōst' sē' zən) **Postseason** *events happen* **after** *a season has ended.* (adjective)
Many **postseason** parties were held to honor the winning team.

4. **predict** (prĭ dĭkt') *When we* **predict** *we say that something will happen* **before** *it actually happens.* (verb)
It is hard to **predict** what the weather will be like next week.

5. **prejudice** (prĕj' ə dĭs) **Prejudice** *is a negative judgment or opinion formed* **before** *knowing or examining the facts.* (noun)
At one time, there was a great deal of **prejudice** against women in business, but this is changing.

6. **premature** (prē' mə tŏor') *Something that is* **premature** *happens or is done* **before** *it is ready.* (adjective)
Injuries forced the hockey player into a **premature** retirement.

7. **preteen** (prē tēn') *A* **preteen** *is a person between nine and twelve* **before** *that person becomes a teenager.* (noun)
The **preteen** attended a concert with his dad.

8. **preview** (prē' vyoō') *A* **preview** *is a showing of something* **before** *a regular showing.* (noun)
Special guests were invited to the sneak **preview** of the movie.

Draw a line between each vocabulary word and its definition.

1. posterity	after the season
2. postpone	those who come after
3. prejudice	put off
4. postseason	judging without facts
5. preview	tell what will happen
6. predict	early showing

B All the boldfaced words in the passage below include the prefixes *pre-* or *post-*. Read the passage. Then answer the questions that follow.

Wilma Rudolph—Champion Runner

As fast as lightning—don't blink, or you'll miss her! These were the words people used to describe champion runner Wilma Rudolph. The story of her life shows that if a person wants to succeed, no one can **predict** how far that person can go.

Wilma Rudolph was a **premature** baby born into a family of 22 children. As a child, she was often sick. When she developed polio, Wilma lost the use of her left leg. She had to **postpone** going to school until she was seven. Because of the **prejudice** of people at that time, Wilma, who was African American, could not be treated by a hospital near her home. She had to travel 50 miles from home for medical care.

Wilma had to use crutches to walk when she was a child, but she was determined to walk without them. One day, when she was 11, the **preteen** surprised everyone by walking into church without her crutches. That was just a **preview** of things to come. Soon Wilma began to run.

In high school, Wilma played basketball during the year and helped her family during the **postseason** summer period. Wilma also became a star runner. When she was only 16, she won an Olympic bronze medal. Then, in the 1960 Olympics, Wilma Rudolph became the first American woman to win three gold medals in running.

After Wilma graduated from college, she taught at the high school she had attended. She also became a speaker and writer. Wilma Rudolph left several important gifts to **posterity**, including the Wilma Rudolph Foundation, which now provides free coaching and tutoring to poor children.

WORD LIST

posterity

postpone

postseason

predict

prejudice

premature

preteen

preview

1. What do you think was Wilma Rudolph's most important accomplishment? _____

_____

_____

2. Use two of the following words to write about Wilma Rudolph's life: **premature, postpone,** or **prejudice.**

_____

_____

C In one list, put the words that have the meaning "before." In the other list, put the words that have the meaning "after."

Before	After
_____	_____
_____	_____
_____	_____
_____	_____

D Write the word from the word list that best completes each sentence.

1. You know you want to see a movie because, at the theater, you saw a few short scenes from it in a _____ .

2. Your little brother is only four years old, but he wants a two-wheeled bicycle already. You know he can't ride it. The time for his wish to come true has not yet come. His wish is _____ .

3. You want to go swimming. But because it is raining, you have to wait. You must _____ it.

4. Just from reading the first few paragraphs, you can tell that this story will have a happy ending. You can _____ it.

OTHER FORMS

postponement

prediction

prejudiced

prejudicial

prematurely

previewing

E Complete each sentence with a phrase that makes sense. Note that some other forms of the vocabulary words have been used.

1. During the **postseason,** the baseball players _____

_____ .

2. **Preteens** often _____

_____ .

3. We must protect the environment for **posterity** because _____

_____ .

4. **Prejudice** can happen when _____

_____ .

5. My **prediction** for next year is that _____

_____ .

ENRICHMENT WORDS

Here are two more words that have the prefix *pre-*, which means "before."

1. **precaution** (prĭ kô' shən) *A* **precaution** *is an action taken to guard against danger, error, or accident.* (noun)
Getting a vaccination to protect against measles is an important **precaution.**

2. **preface** (prĕf' ĭs) *A* **preface** *is a part of a book that comes before the main part and introduces it.* (noun)
In the **preface,** the author told about the time period of the story.

A vaccine is a precaution.

OFF THE PAGE

Predictions play a big part of some people's jobs. Weather forecasters earn a living by predicting the weather. Sportswriters predict who will win the most games. Choose an example of a person who makes predictions. Write about why predictions are important in a particular job. Also tell what the person might use to make predictions and how accurate they are likely to be.

All Together
prefix co-

comrades

A The prefix *co-* means " with" or "together." Some other spellings of this prefix are *col-*, *com-*, *con-*, and *cor-*. The words below all include this prefix.

1. **coexist** (kō' ĭg zĭst') **Coexist** *means to live together peacefully.* (verb)
People **coexist** with bacteria that help them to digest food.

2. **coincidence** (kō ĭn' sĭ dəns) *A* **coincidence** *is something that happens by accident; things come together by chance.* (noun)
By **coincidence,** my cousin and I have the same birthday.

3. **collect** (kə lĕkt') *To* **collect** *is to gather things together.* (verb)
I **collect** stamps from African nations.

4. **collide** (kə līd') *When things* **collide,** *they bump into each other; they come together.* (verb)
When two trains **collide,** people may be hurt.

5. **comrade** (kŏm' răd') *A* **comrade** *is a friend; you do things with a comrade.* (noun)
The three **comrades** asked to be in the same cabin at overnight camp.

6. **concur** (kən kûr') *To* **concur** *is to have the same opinion; to agree with another person's opinion.* (verb)
All the students **concur** that they need a longer lunch period.

7. **coordinate** (kō ôr' dn āt') *To* **coordinate** *is to work together or to help people work together.* (verb)
The principal had to **coordinate** the school bus schedules so that every student would arrive at school on time.

8. **correspond** (kôr' ĭ spŏnd') *When things* **correspond,** *they are very similar to each other; they agree with each other.* (verb)
The gills of a fish **correspond** to the lungs of a person.

Draw a line between each vocabulary word and its definition.

1. coordinate   friend

2. comrade   work together

3. coexist   to be in agreement with

4. correspond   live peacefully together

The boldfaced words in the passage below all contain the prefix *co-*. Read the passage. Then answer the questions that follow.

Canada Geese—A Study in Cooperation

Have you ever watched geese make a V in the sky as they fly? By doing this, each goose can **coordinate** its flight with the rest of the group. The geese never **collide;** they always seem to be just the right distance from each other. Scientists **concur** that the V shape is not a **coincidence.** The V helps to make the force of the wind less for each goose.

Perhaps you've heard the honking of flying geese. Geese travel in family groups, and young geese recognize the honks of their parents. Honking helps the family to stay together. You might say that the honks **correspond** to a human mother calling her children to keep them together while on a hike.

Each year in the fall, many Canada geese **collect** at Horicon Marsh in Wisconsin. The birds fly south from Canada to where the Ohio River meets the Mississippi River. They spend the winter in this place because there is lots of food. Then in the spring, they journey back to Canada.

Geese in a V formation are usually traveling a long distance. They travel high, where the air is cool. They often fly as fast as 45 or 50 miles per hour. A goose flying low and alone is probably just looking for a meal. Geese mate for life, and if one goose is hurt, its mate will often drop out of the formation to stay with it.

Human beings would do well to learn from the Canada Goose how to **coexist** better with **comrades** and family members.

1. Why do geese fly in a V-formation? Use a new word in your answer.

_____

_____

2. Write two sentences to tell important facts about Canada Geese. Use at least one new word in each sentence.

_____

_____

C Choose the right word from the word list for each sentence. Write the word on the line.

1. Ricardo likes to _____ seashells. *(coexist/collect)*

2. When an SUV and a small car _____, the car will probably have more damage. *(correspond/collide)*

3. Rosie was asked to _____ the contests and games at the school picnic. *(coordinate/concur)*

4. When I saw Jane at the airport, I thought she had come to meet me, but it was just a _____ that she was there. *(coincidence/comrade)*

5. I _____ with the judge's opinion that this is the best apple pie. *(coexist/concur)*

D Complete the crossword puzzle, using words from the word list.

Across

1. Gather things together
4. Match; are like each other

Down

1. friend
2. bump; hit
3. I _____ with your opinion

Name _____

Date _____

coexistence

coincidental

collection

collector

collision

coordination

E Complete each sentence with a phrase that makes sense. Note that some other forms of the vocabulary words have been used.

1. In a **collision**, _____

_____ .

2. If you **concur**, _____

_____ .

3. An example of something that is interesting to **collect** is _____

_____ .

4. A person riding a bike should have good **coordination** of arms

and legs because _____

_____ .

5. It was **coincidental** that my friend and I _____

_____ .

ENRICHMENT WORDS

Here are two more words with the prefix *co-*, meaning "together."

1. **communal** (kə myōō' nəl) *Something* **communal** *is shared by a community*. (adjective)

   Many years ago, Swiss people baked bread in **communal** ovens.

2. **composite** (kəm pŏz' ĭt) *Something that is a* **composite** *is made from several different things.* (adjective)

   Police listened to many different descriptions of the criminal, and then an artist drew a **composite** sketch.

a composite sketch

OFF THE PAGE

Write a paragraph that describes the type of comrade you would like to take on a trip. Be sure you describe both the type of person and the type of trip you would like to take.

LESSON 29

"Bad" Beginnings
prefixes mis-, anti-

Arctic

Antarctic

A The prefix *mis-* means "bad" or "wrong."
Sometimes it means "badly" or "wrongly."
The prefix *anti-* means "against" or "opposite."
The words below include these word parts.

1. **antagonism** (ăn tăg' ə nĭz' əm)
Antagonism *is a feeling of hatred or of being* **against** *someone.* (noun)
We should compete in sports without feeling **antagonism** toward other teams.

2. **Antarctica** (ănt ärk' tĭ kə) **Antarctica** *is the region around the South Pole; it is* **opposite** *the Arctic (or North Pole).* (noun)
The lowest temperature on earth, minus 128.6 degrees Fahrenheit, was recorded in **Antarctica.**

3. **antiseptic** (ăn' tĭ sĕp' tĭk) *An* **antiseptic** *is a medicine that kills or acts* **against** *germs.* (noun)
Mom put an **antiseptic** on my cut to prevent infection.

4. **antisocial** (ăn' tē sō' shəl) *Something that is* **antisocial** *is* **against** *the good of society.* (adjective)
Violence is **antisocial** behavior.

5. **misbehave** (mĭs' bĭ hāv') *To* **misbehave** *is to act or behave badly.* (verb)
The principal will talk to students who **misbehave** during the assembly.

6. **misfortune** (mĭs fôr' chən)
Misfortune *is bad luck, or bad fortune.* (noun)
The family suffered **misfortune** when an earthquake destroyed their home.

7. **mismatch** (mĭs' măch') *When there is a* **mismatch,** *something does* **not** *belong or match with something else.* (noun)
A red sock paired with a white sock is a **mismatch.**

8. **mistrust** (mĭs trŭst') *To* **mistrust** *is to doubt or suspect, to* **not** *trust.* (verb)
We **mistrust** people who lie and cheat.

Draw a line between each vocabulary word and its definition.

1. misbehave — lack of trust
2. antisocial — not matched
3. mismatch — behave badly
4. mistrust — against society
5. antiseptic — South Pole region
6. Antarctica — medicine
7. antagonism — bad luck
8. misfortune — hatred

© Great Source DO NOT COPY

Each of the boldfaced words in the passage has the prefix *mis-* or *anti-*. Read the passage. Then answer the questions that follow.

Ann Bancroft—Explorer of the Arctic and Antarctic

When she was 12, Ann Bancroft loved to read about the great explorers of **Antarctica.** She wanted to see the place for herself, so she began to develop her winter camping skills. In the cold Minnesota winters, she often slept outside in a tent.

As a child, Ann had a learning disability that prevented her from reading easily in school. But she turned this **misfortune** to her advantage. Because of her problems in school, Ann learned to be a hard worker.

Today, she is a top explorer of the Arctic and Antarctica. Bancroft was the first woman to travel across the ice to the North Pole. Then, in 1993 she led the first women's team to ski to the South Pole.

Bancroft chose her team carefully to make sure that there would be no personality **mismatches.** The women on the team had to cooperate and no one could **misbehave** in any way. **Mistrust** could add greatly to problems in the journey and **antagonism** could risk everyone's life.

On the Antarctic trip, the women skied over 600 miles, pulling heavy sleds. Despite heavy clothes, they experienced frostbite. They also had to protect against the strong sun that shone day and night in the Antarctic summer. They had to carry a lot of supplies, including **antiseptics,** to help prevent infections. Although they ate huge meals, they still lost weight from skiing ten hours each day.

While skiing, the women usually traveled single file, taking turns in the lead to break the force of the wind for others. They even had to sit down in single file, so it was hard to talk. Bancroft reports that such lonely experiences can cause **antisocial** behavior. She tried to train for the trip by herself so she could become used to feeling alone.

antagonism

Antarctica

antiseptic

antisocial

misbehave

misfortune

mismatch

mistrust

1. How did Ann Bancroft's childhood prepare her to follow her dream?

_____

_____

2. Choose two of the boldfaced words to describe some possible problems in a long, difficult journey to the South Pole.

_____

_____

_____

C Choose the word to best complete each sentence. Write the word on the line.

1. My little sister will probably _____ at the movie by talking too loud. *(mismatch/misbehave)*

2. It was Craig's _____ to be called on to give the answer to the hard math problem. *(misfortune/antagonism)*

3. Our new neighbor always ignores us when we say hello. He seems _____ . *(mismatch/antisocial)*

4. The nurse put _____ on my cut finger so it wouldn't get infected. *(mistrust/antiseptic)*

5. There's a lot of _____ between our cat and our neighbor's cat. *(Antarctica/antagonism)*

D Write the vocabulary word that is a synonym for the words in each group.

1. doubt, question, suspect   _____

2. disaster, bad luck, calamity   _____

3. unfriendly, alone, unsociable   _____

4. dislike, hatred, bad feeling   _____

5. act up, carry on, vandalize   _____

E Complete each sentence with a phrase that makes sense. Note that some other forms of the vocabulary words have been used.

1. Someone who is **antagonistic** is _____ _____ .

2. You might wear **mismatched** clothes because _____ _____ .

3. People who go to **Antarctica** _____ _____ .

4. People who are **antisocial** _____ _____ .

5. If I **mistrusted** someone, _____ _____ .

ENRICHMENT WORDS

Here are two more words with prefixes. One has the prefix *anti-*. The other has the prefix *mis-*. How do the prefixes help you figure out what the words mean?

1. **antidote** (ăn' tĭ dōt') *An* **antidote** *is something that works against a poison or a bad state.* (noun)

   Sunshine can be an **antidote** to a bad mood.

2. **mislead** (mĭs lēd') *When we* **mislead** *somebody, we give them a wrong idea.* (verb)

   I won't **mislead** you by telling you that this will be an easy job.

OFF THE PAGE

Antisocial behavior can be a problem in schools and neighborhoods. Make a poster that addresses **antisocial** behavior in one of those settings. Make clear on your poster what the problem is and what your solution is.

LESSON 30

REVIEW:
Lessons 26-29

In this lesson, you will review the words and skills you have learned in the last four lessons. This will help you to remember them when you read and write.

A **MATCHING WORDS AND DEFINITIONS** Write the word from the list that matches each definition.

> posterity   prejudice   correspond   antiseptic   antagonism

1. equal or very similar _____

2. negative judgment formed before knowing the facts _____

3. people not born yet; those who come after _____

4. feeling of hatred or of being against someone_____

5. medicine that acts against germs _____

B **USING WORDS IN CONTEXT** Use the words in each box to complete the paragraphs.

> correspond   coordinate   coincidence   collect

My sister is planning to **(1)** _____ details about our family history. Using the computer, she'll create a book of photographs and family stories. I'm going to help her write captions that **(2)** _____ to the photos. By **(3)** _____, our cousin has also started an album, so we're going to **(4)** _____ our efforts.

© Great Source DO NOT COPY

predict   concur   antagonism   coexist

You have good ideas about starting a community garden, and I

(5) _____ with them. When they work on the garden,

neighbors from different cultures will get to know each other. Different

groups will discover that they can (6) _____ happily.

People will get along, and (7) _____ may just disappear

from the neighborhood. I (8) _____ great harvests from

this community garden!

C **WRITING SENTENCES** Choose two of the words on
each line to use in sentences. You can change the form of the word
if you like. (For example, *collect* may be changed to *collection*, or
misbehave may be changed to *misbehavior*.)

1. **collect   postpone   misfortune**

   _____

   _____

2. **concur   mistrust   predict**

   _____

   _____

3. **coordinate   antisocial   preteen**

   _____

   _____

4. **coexist   preview   misbehave**

   _____

   _____

5. **comrade   Antarctica   posterity**

   _____

   _____

D **REVIEWING PREFIXES** Complete these sentences with a word or phrase that makes sense.

1. An **antiseptic** is used to _____ .

2. A **coincidence** is when two things _____ .

3. When two things are a **mismatch,** they _____ .

4. **Postseason** events happen _____ .

5. Animals that **coexist** live _____ .

6. **Antagonism** is a feeling of _____ .

7. **Antisocial** behavior is behavior that _____ .

8. To **coordinate** an activity is to _____ .

9. If you **mistrust** someone, you _____ .

10. Someone who is a **preteen** is about _____ years old.

E **TEST-TAKING STRATEGIES** In an **analogy,** both pairs of words are related in the same way.

Strategy: Words can be related by their structure, or how they are formed. Look at this example. How is the first pair of words related?

behave : misbehave : : _____ : postseason *(season/postpone)*

Here's one way to think through this analogy:

"*Behave* is a root word. *Misbehave* is the root word plus a prefix. Since *postseason* is a root word plus a prefix, the missing word must be *season*. *Postpone* does not fit this pattern."

Directions: Write the word that completes each analogy on the line. Remember that different types of analogies can be used.

1. teen : preteen : : _____ : preview *(see/view)*

2. use : misuse : : step : _____ *(misstep/stepping)*

3. collide : bump : : agree : _____ *(collect/concur)*

4. clean : dirty : : late : _____ *(premature/prejudice)*

5. biologist : scientist : : friend : _____ *(laboratory/comrade)*

TEST-TAKING STRATEGIES On a **multiple-choice** test, usually two or three answers seem like good choices, but only one answer is correct.

Strategy: After you decide on the best answer, read the whole question through with each choice to be sure you chose the correct one. Then carefully fill in the bubble next to the answer.

Directions: Fill in the bubble next to the best answer to each question.

1. What is a synonym for *premature?*
   (A) old   (B) young   (C) early   (D) late

2. What is an antiseptic used for?
   (A) as a drink   (C) as a laundry soap
   (B) to prevent infection (D) to clean floors

3. Which of the following best describes the location of Antarctica?
   (A) South Pole region   (C) Argentina
   (B) North Pole region   (D) near Spain

4. What is another word for *doubt?*
   (A) jeer   (B) mistrust   (C) trouble   (D) misfortune

5. Which of the following is a good reason to postpone a baseball game?
   (A) heavy rain   (C) free tickets
   (B) a sunny day   (D) sold-out crowd

ENRICHMENT WORDS

Draw a line between each Enrichment Word and its definition.

1. precaution   shared by a community
2. communal   action to guard against danger
3. antidote   made from different things
4. preface   give someone a wrong idea
5. composite   something that works against poison
6. mislead   introduction to a book